# "I'm going to have you, Dale. You're mine."

Jos's voice was thick against her hair as she felt his hands moving possessively over her body; the sensitive sculptor's fingers seeking and finding nerve endings she hadn't known existed, taking control of her senses. The heat rose in her, reaching out to take over her whole being. When he stopped she felt deprived.

"I don't belong to you," she whispered, trying to regain her control. "I don't belong to anyone."

"But you're going to. If it's marriage you want, then we'll get married."

Dale stared at him in blank confusion. "We don't have any basis for marriage," she got out at last, and saw his lips twist.

"What do you consider lacking?"

"Love, for one thing." Her reply was emphatic.

"Is that all?" he asked. "It's an overrated emotion, anyway."

## KAY THORPE
is also the author of these

# *Harlequin Presents*

and these

# *Harlequin Romances*

# KAY THORPE

## floodtide

*Harlequin Books*

TORONTO • LONDON • LOS ANGELES • AMSTERDAM
SYDNEY • HAMBURG • PARIS • STOCKHOLM • ATHENS • TOKYO

Harlequin Presents edition published April 1981
ISBN 0-373-10425-1

Original hardcover edition published in 1981
by Mills & Boon Limited

# CHAPTER ONE

IF THE HOUSE DIDN'T SHOW inside the next ten minutes she was going to give up and go back to Market Deeping for the night, Dale promised herself resignedly, peering through the streaming windshield at the flat Lincolnshire countryside. The low, scudding cloud allowed little light to filter through, turning the afternoon to premature evening and the fens themselves to featureless gray, drab and depressing on the eye.

After nearly a week of rain the weather must surely be due for a change of some kind. Perhaps tomorrow would bring a return to the blue skies and breezy sunshine one normally associated with spring. Dale hoped so anyway. She had allowed herself only three days in which to complete this assignment, and that included the return trip to London.

She had probably been a fool to accept the challenge in the first place, she acknowledged ruefully. Many had tried and none had succeeded. Jos Blakeman granted interviews to no one, maintaining his right to personal privacy while satisfying the overgrowing demand for his work. A part of Dale could understand and even appreciate that need, but it wasn't her job to let such notions sway her. When Ben Reynolds said do, one either did or stood down for someone else who could.

Not that anyone else had been all that eager to step into her shoes. She was here at all because she had needed to demonstrate to Ben that Keely Weston was not the only female he had ever employed with stamina and perseverence enough to tackle the impossible—although she had to admit that stowing away on board a boat for a dangerous trip into unchartered regions still gave the other a certain one-upmanship. She had come out of it pretty well, by all accounts. Marriage to a man such as Greg Stirling was reputed to be could hardly fail to be exciting.

Persuading Jos Blakeman to talk to her seemed tame enough on the surface but could prove no less hazardous than Keely's venture. The last one to try breaking in on that valued privacy had finished up on his ear, and he was no lightweight, either. The few available photographs of the sculptor showed an angular-featured man in his mid thirties who looked anything but artistic on first sight. It was only the eyes that belied the image. Even on paper they seemed to penetrate right through one. Which didn't make her plan of campaign so hopeful. He would probably see right through that, too. Still, she could only try.

Was that a glimmer of light up ahead? She switched off her headlights for a moment in order to make sure. Yes, there it was. Through the slanting rain, she could even make out the square shape of the house around it, standing back from the narrow roadway with neither fence nor wall to define the boundaries of its land. It had to be the right place. According to what they had told her in the last village, there was no other house for a couple of miles.

With the headlights still switched off, Dale pulled onto the side of the road to sort out her next move. Putting the car into the ditch was no problem, but doing so without serious damage might prove difficult. That however, was a chance she would have to take. She needed an excuse to get into the house, and what better one than an urgent request to use the telephone in order to summon help in pulling the vehicle clear again? That the house didn't have a telephone she already knew, but Jos Blakeman wouldn't know that. He would be forced to take her story at face value.

And then? Dale pulled a wry face. That was something she couldn't plan. It all depended on the man's reactions. If he insisted on running her to the nearest garage himself then there would be little she could do but accept her failure. From where she sat she couldn't see a car, but he must certainly have one. Without transport he would be stranded out here. There would be outbuildings around the back no doubt. An offer of hospitality until morning seemed unlikely in the face of what she knew about him, but it was all she could hope for. Even then it might not be long enough. Getting a man of his kind to loosen up took time.

Going in now might prove her biggest mistake, she reasoned. The longer she waited, the more chance she stood of spending the night. Despite the time of year, in this weather it would be full dark by seven o'clock or so. That gave her a couple of hours to waste away, perhaps three if she wanted darkness to add plausibility to her plea of getting lost. Boring in the extreme, yet worth it if it produced the desired result. There was some coffee left in her thermos, and although damp, the air wasn't too cold. She could manage if she put her mind to it. She had to manage.

She left the lights switched off, confident that the car could not be seen at this distance and this angle from the house. Sipping the last of the coffee she wondered what Roger would say if he could see her now. As her fiancé, she supposed he had merited the truth, but there was no way he would have condoned any of this. What he would really like was for her to get out of journalism altogether, only that was one thing she refused to do. He had his job and she had hers. Surely two people in love could manage to reconcile their life-style to accommodate both?

There was more to it than that, she knew. She wore Roger's ring yet the doubts were present in her mind. Did she really love him, or was she simply attracted by his looks, his standard of living, his very confidence in himself and all he stood for? When she was with him she could tell herself it was surely enough. It was only at moments like this when she had time to sit and think that her emotions became so mixed.

Yet what was it she wanted in addition to what she already had? Perhaps Roger did appear a little lacking in passion at times, but no doubt that would change once they were married and able to make love without the restraints imposed upon them now. Restraints she herself dictated, she was bound to admit. If they were going to go to bed together it had to be because neither of them could control the need a moment longer. Roger never lost control. Even when he told her how much he wanted her there was always that element of reserve in him.

So what she really wanted was to be swept off her feet, Dale reflected dryly. Total abandonment from both sides. Yet the kind of man who might satisfy that particular need in her would more than likely be lacking in other departments. She wanted the best of both worlds, and that was all too rarely possible. Why not settle for a more than adequate compromise, the way her mother had? She had been happy enough on the face of it.

Looking back, Dale could scarcely remember a time when she hadn't been aware of the differences in temperament between her parents. Her father was like Roger in many ways: a man to admire and respect in addition to love. Yet, as in Roger, there had always been a sense of something held back, and her mother must have been aware of it, too, even though she had never shown it. She followed where her husband led, accepted her role in his life. It was only on rare occasions that Dale had caught that certain wry quality in her smile, and only in later years that she had come fully to understand it. Lack of complete fulfillment was one way of putting it, she supposed. She and her mother shared the same need for totality in emotion. With Roger she would never know it, and that was something *she* had to accept if she wanted him at all.

Lifting her left hand she regarded the sparkling hoop of diamonds thoughtfully for a long moment, then suddenly slid the ring off and pushed it into her handbag. Forget about Roger for the present. That decision could come later when she had this job all tied up. If might be a better word, but she refused to even consider it. She was going to have that interview if it was the last thing she ever did.

Journalism hadn't always been in her blood. She had tried a number of other jobs first. The chance to work on the fashion page of a monthly magazine had come about almost by accident through a friend of a friend, but from there she had never looked back. *World Magazine* was the ultimate for her, a place at the very top of her particular tree, and at twenty-three that couldn't be bad. She had been six months on it and had enjoyed every moment.

She was even enjoying this now in a peculiar kind of

way, snug and secure in a rented car with the rain hissing past the windows and nothing for miles but that house out there. In a little while she was going to arrange to have that accident, and then look out Mr. Jos Blakeman! The frontal approach had failed on other occasions so this was all that was left. Just a little longer until it was dark.

She awoke with a jerk, stifling a groan at the stiffness in her neck as she lifted her head from its resting place on the seat back. It was still raining, but there was an odd difference to the sound of it—one she couldn't quite place. The darkness outside was broken only by the dim glow from the window some few hundred yards distant. Dale fancied she saw a shadow cross the oblong but it was difficult to be sure through the rain.

The dashboard clock was luminous. She stared at it in some disbelief. Half-past eight! That meant she had slept for a full three hours! Perhaps not so surprising considering her early start this morning and late night before it, yet one would have thought the discomfort alone would have been enough to waken her earlier.

Well, at least it had passed the time on, she thought, rubbing at her neck. It was both late enough and nasty enough to make the chances of Jos Blakeman wanting to set out with the car fairly unlikely. All she needed now was the right spot for her "accident," which admittedly might have been better chosen by daylight.

Except that she might have been seen peering into the ditch, mightn't she? That would hardly have enhanced her chances. She would just have to take the risk.

Reaching out a hand to the ignition, she paused, suddenly realizing how stupid she had been parking the car this close to the house. The sound of the engine would carry that far, and not a growing note as it should be were she just approaching. Nothing else for it, she decided resignedly, mentally kicking herself. If the point drew comment she would simply have to play dumb and pretend the weather must have blocked out the sound.

Despite the warmth of her tweed jacket she found herself shivering a little. Even the floor of the car felt damp, striking up through her shoes. It *was* damp, she realized scarcely a second later, feeling the carpet squelch as she moved her foot toward the clutch. What on earth!

The water was just about level with the doorsill when she opened the door, a dark, lapping menace stretching out of sight, its surface hissing to the falling rain. Dale gazed at it in dismay, hardly able to take in the implications in that first moment. The river must have breached its banks for flooding of this depth. She had known the Welland was somewhere close by, but not this close! There was no telling where the narrow road ended and the peat fields began, ditches and all ironed out by the water. Even as she sat there it began lapping over the rim of the sill, bringing her suddenly alive to the fact that it was still rising, and swiftly.

Closing the door again shut out all but a trickle for the moment, but she obviously couldn't go on sitting here for much longer. Driving was equally out of the question. Even if the water stopped rising, her chances of being able to keep to the road surface beneath it were minimal.

Which left only one alternative. An ironical little smile touched her lips. She had wanted an excuse to get into the house over there hadn't she? Here was a perfect one ready engineered. With the water still rising she could finish up stranded for a couple of days. What a story that would make!

Not one Roger would care for, came the thought, and Dale sighed. He would have been horrified to know she contemplated spending even one night under Jos Blakeman's roof, much less two, simply because the latter was male. For herself, she had no concern on that score. When working toward a show such as the one due to be presented in about six weeks' time, the sculptor was apparently in the habit of isolating himself from all outside influences—including women friends. Hence this place miles from anywhere. He was hardly going to bother himself with her just because she happened to be there. His energies would be geared to his work.

Her shoes were already soaked, and in any case she didn't fancy wading through that lot out there bare footed. She rolled her trouser bottoms up to her knees, and seized her small overnight bag from the back seat before gingerly opening the door again, gasping as cold water poured into the car over her feet. The insurance people weren't going to be too pleased, but there was nothing she could do about that. Her main concern at the moment had to be in reaching the house.

She found the road surface almost at knee depth, standing up unsteadily and holding onto the roof edge with one hand while she swung her bag against the door to close it. A waste of time considering, but it might keep some of it out. One thing was certain, she wasn't going to be driving the car anywhere again.

How she was going to get away from here when the time came was another problem she put to the back of her mind. The Lincolnshire fens had been flooded before. Rescue facilities must be available. She only hoped they didn't come too soon.

Wading through the black water proved more difficult than she had imagined. Before she had gone three steps her rolled trousers were soaked and her shoes like soggy lumps on her feet. Thank goodness she had had the sense to wear flats. Feeling her way through this little lot in heels would have invited disaster. Not that it would have made all that much difference, with the rain already penetrating her jacket and dripping from the ends of her hair. She was going to look like a drowned rat by the time she did reach the house.

If she ever did reach it. She was opposite to it now, but with no idea just where the earth bridge marking its access across the ditch might be, although she had seen it from the car earlier. There was nothing to do but to feel with her feet as she went forward, and hope for the best. It had to be wide enough to take a car, so she surely couldn't miss it if she were careful. Slipping into the ditch on either side would be no joke. The water down there must be more than three feet deep.

She didn't slip, but the track itself sloped slightly downward from the other side of the ditch, bringing the water over her knees before it leveled off. She was so wet now that it barely mattered. Grimly she hugged the overnight case to her chest, determined to keep a few dry clothes to her name. At least there was no chance of Jos Blakeman shutting the door in her face now. One wouldn't turn a dog away in conditions such as these.

The door itself was shut tight, with what felt like sandbags piled up against the bottom. So Jos Blakeman had suspected this might be coming—which seemed to suggest that the shopkeeper she had asked for directions in the village back there might have had some idea, too; yet he had uttered no word of warning. Probably he had thought that anyone idiot enough to be traveling through fen country in weather such as this deserved all they got. Right now Dale could almost agree with him.

Knocking seemed incongruous on the face of it, but
she did it anyway, stifling an involuntary giggle in the
realization that hysteria lurked not so far away. There
were heavy splashing sounds from inside, then a casement of the window a couple of feet away was flung
back and a head was poked through.

"Who the hell is that?" demanded the owner in a
tone Dale found distinctly unwelcoming. "What the
devil do you think you're doing?"

"Drowning if I stand out here much longer," she
said, shivering as she spoke. "My car is back there along
the road. I had to leave it. Can you help me?"

A ridiculous question under the circumstances. He obviously thought so, too, judging from the expression on
the lean face. "You'll have to come in this way," he said.
"I'm keeping the level in here as low as possible for as
long as possible, and that means not opening the door."

The window was a good four feet from the ground.
"How?" Dale asked without moving.

The head disappeared and there was the sound of further splashing. A moment later a stool was poked out
through the casement.

"Come and get a hold of this," said the voice from
behind it. "It'll give you enough height to get a knee
across the sill."

Dale waded forward to take the stool from him,
almost dropping her bag in the process. "Will you take
this?" she said, lifting it up to the waiting hand. "I
can't manage both."

Finding a level base for the stool to rest on was one
problem, climbing onto it an even greater one. She felt
her panty hose tear as the rough edge of the wood
snagged them, and clutched hastily at the windowsill to
stop herself from wobbling over.

The same hand that had taken her bag from her now seized her wrist in a painfully firm grip, keeping her upright by sheer brute force as it dragged her bodily through the window. Then her wrist was released and both hands came under her armpits, lifting her clear of the sill.

Dale had a fleeting impression of lean muscularity as he lowered her to what would have been the floor in better times. He was a good six inches taller than she was, and broad enough in the shoulder to blot out the room behind him from her view. The hands under her arms had a totally impersonal feel to them, despite the pressure of his wrists against the side of her breasts. He released her immediately, looking down at her with an expression she found anything but reassuring.

"I won't ask you what you're doing touring the fens in this weather," he said sourly. "It's enough that you're here at all. I suppose you realize we're both stuck with it for the present?"

"Unfortunately, yes," she said, refusing to flinch from the cold-blue scrutiny. "I was trying to reach Spalding."

"In the dark?"

"It wasn't dark when I set off. I took a wrong turn somewhere—got off the main road and couldn't find my way back to it. Then this lot came."

"There was a flood warning," Jos Blakeman responded. "Don't you listen to the radio?"

"My car doesn't have one." She shivered again, feeling the water cold around her knees. It was perhaps six inches shallower in here. So much for not opening the door. "Do you think we could get out of this?" she asked, trying not to sound sarcastic about it. "I'm soaked through, and frozen to the marrow!"

"Upstairs," he said, and stood to one side to let her pass. "It's a clear passage through. I managed to shift most of the loose stuff before the river went."

They were in a large living room, Dale saw, with the staircase going up from one side of it and a couple more doors in the rear wall. Her bag rested on a big, old-fashioned sideboard a few feet away. There was no shade on the central light fixture and even the low wattage of the bulb hanging there failed to conceal the general shabbiness of the place. A sofa had its cushions just clear of the water, though not for long judging from the way the latter was coming in around the doorframe.

"At least you still have electricity," she commented as they waded across to the stairs. "I suppose underground cables are safe enough even in floods."

"Providing the water doesn't get into a fuse box," he came back dryly. "And we've only the lighting. I isolated the sockets to stop the other fuses from blowing. Luckily the fuse box is high enough to stay clear. Otherwise it would be back to oil lamps for the duration."

"Clever." Her tone stopped just short of irony. "I wouldn't have imagined...."

They had reached the stairs now and were clear of the water on the third tread. "Imagined what?" he prompted when she failed to complete the sentence.

"Nothing." Dale drew in a steadying breath. She had been about to say that she wouldn't have imagined an artist knowing about such mundane things, yet she wasn't supposed to know his identity. If he once guessed that she did know he might easily start suspecting her motives for being here. "You just don't seem the type, that's all," she tagged on lamely.

He looked at her with lifted brows for a moment, one arm stretched across her to the bannister, blocking her further progress: dark brows to match the thick dark hair falling over his forehead to meet them. There was a sardonic twist to the firmly cut mouth. "Type for what?" he insisted.

"To be living out here in the back of beyond," she implemented, seeing no way out of it. "You are on your own, aren't you?"

"That's right." His eyes had narrowed a fraction, the blueness taking on a steely quality. "You don't know me?"

"Should I?" Her heart was hammering against her rib cage, making it difficult to keep her breathing even and unalarmed.

His expression didn't alter. "Maybe!" He paused, watching her. "The name is Blakeman. Joseph Blakeman."

Dale had her face ready for it. Now she let puzzlement show in her eyes. "Is that supposed to mean something to me?"

"I thought it might."

A pause, then a little dawning enlightenment. "You mean you're somebody famous or something?"

"Or something," he agreed. He seemed to relax, a smile touching his lips. "How about you?"

"Dale Ryland," she supplied, and went straight into her prepared story. "I'm heading up the coast to Hull. I've an aunt there. Somebody said I should make a detour to see the Spalding Carnival and the tulip fields."

"In this weather?"

"It could have cleared up."

"It could." He took his hand away from the banister,

indicating that she go on up ahead of him with an in-
clination of his head. "You'd better get out of those wet
things before you catch pneumonia. There's enough hot
water if you'd like a bath. The water heater is on a different circuit."

"I'd love one," she said gratefully, moving in front.
"I'm just sorry to be such a nuisance, that's all."

He made no answer, obviously seeing no call for
gallant denial. He was putting up with her descent on
him because he had no choice, but he wasn't going to
make out it delighted him. Dale could hardly blame him
for feeling that way. She could even feel a faint sense of
guilt at her deception. But not enough to force a confession, that was for sure. She had a job to do and she was
going to do it, to the best of her ability.

Besides, there was no knowing which way the man
might jump if she did tell him the truth. The artistic
temperament was notoriously unpredictable. If it came
out at all it had to be later when she could better judge
his likely reactions. Obviously it would be better if she
had his go-ahead for the projected article, but regardless, she intended to go through with her plan. The very
fact of her having spent a couple of days marooned with
Jos Blakeman would be enough to sell it to Ben, official
interview or not. If she could also ferret some background material out of him in the process, it could only
be to the good.

There were four doors leading off the narrow landing. One of the middle ones was open, the room beyond
overwhelmed by the hodgepodge of household items
piled into it. A kerosene heater sent out a welcome glow
of warmth.

Jos Blakeman opened another door on the left,
switching on a light to reveal an old-fashioned bath and

basin. They were at least clean, the bath large enough to lie down in without touching either end. The thought of stepping into piping-hot water more than compensated for the bleakness of the decor.

"Clean towels in the airing cupboard there," advised her host, dropping her bag to the linoleumed floor. "Not much room, I'm afraid, but I daresay you'll manage. I'll be sorting out the mess through there in the meantime, once I get these off."

He was wearing fisherman's thigh boots, she noted for the first time. Ideal for present conditions. "Have you gone through this before?" she asked as he turned to leave her.

"Not to the same extent."

"Then you won't know how long it's likely to take the water to go down?"

"Depends when it stops raining. They're forecasting a break for tomorrow. Providing we don't get any abnormally high tides, I'd say a couple of days before the roads are usable again."

"That long!" Dale barely knew whether to be dismayed or delighted.

"We're below sea level here," he said, "and the ground was already waterlogged. It isn't going to drain away overnight." His smile was dry. "Don't concern yourself too much. They get the boats out in times like these. You'll be rescued before that."

Not for at least twenty-four hours, Dale hoped as he went out, closing the door behind him. He wasn't going to be an easy man to get through to. But then she hadn't expected him to be, had she? She would simply have to try that much harder.

There was no key in the lock. She stood there for a moment contemplating it before giving a dismissive shrug. That was Roger's way of thinking not hers. Jos Blakeman wasn't the type to spend any time peering through keyholes in the hope of catching a glimpse of a naked female. He had probably seen enough in his time to make him blasé about the whole thing.

The water came through in spurts, taking several minutes to fill the bath to a reasonable depth. Dropping her wet clothing in a corner, she slid in blissfully, feeling the warmth stealing back into her bones.

There was a bottle of shampoo on the windowsill. Washing one's hair in the bathwater was hardly hygenic but beggars couldn't be choosers. She lathered well and rinsed by sliding down full length until her head went under, then repeated the process finishing off with a few cupfuls of clean water from the taps.

She had forgotten to take a towel from the cupboard Jos Blakeman had indicated. Fetching one now left a trail of drips across the floor, the coldness of the latter sending her scurrying back to stand on the bathside mat while she dried herself.

The damp-spotted mirror hanging on the wall in front of her reflected a creamy oval of a face and a pair of dark brown eyes flecked with little amber tints that gave them sparkle. At present the hair hanging almost to her shoulders looked dark with moisture. Vigorously toweled it turned to the deep, rich gold that was its natural color, curving softly under at the edges to frame her face. That was better. She felt somewhere approaching normal now. She was going to need all her confidence to face up to the next twenty-four hours.

The sound of movement from the room next door had stopped. When it started again it was on a lower scale as if the bulk of the work was done and only minor adjustments remained. Searching through her case,

Dale drew out a pair of beige jeans and a fine-checked shirt and put them on, sliding her feet into tan, leather sandals. Her wet things she draped across the edge of the bath for the time being, thinking they would need some string or rope to rig up some kind of clothesline overnight.

For the first time she allowed herself to consider the difficulties that might arise. Not sexually; she still wasn't afraid of that. No, the question was where she was going to sleep should there turn out to be only one bed, with no sofa to fall back on. Food was another problem. With the kitchen two feet deep in water how were they going to cook?

The bedroom looked surprisingly cozy when she finally forced herself to go through: the three-quarter bed pushed up against the far wall to make room for the two armchairs that matched the sofa downstairs. There was a table set to one side bearing a cylinder-gas camping stove and a couple of pans, and beside it a box filled to the brim with various items of food, including what looked like a couple of home-baked loaves.

"My daily baked yesterday," said Jos from the floor where he was kneeling to refill the kerosene heater from a large container, anticipating the question trembling on her lips. "Enough to last if we're careful. Are you hungry?"

"Very," Dale admitted, only just acknowledging it. So much had happened in the last couple of hours, food had been farthest from her mind until a few minutes ago. "What did you have in mind?"

"It will have to be a limited menu, I'm afraid, but we won't starve. How does beans and scrambled egg with fresh bread and butter sound?"

"Wonderful!" Dale meant it. At the moment she

wouldn't have exchanged the offer for the finest steak. "Can I get it started?"

"You can cut the bread, I'll do the rest. This time, at any rate." He put down the can and straightened, wiping his hands down the back of his jeans as he turned. The blue eyes took on a sudden new expression, sliding over her slender body in unconcealed appraisal before coming back to her face. "Surprising what a hot bath can do," was all he said, but she was left with an odd sense of breathlessness.

The regard had been purely professional, Dale told herself, watching him move across to the stove. He hadn't been seeing her as a woman at all, simply a series of lines and curves. She knew that was only partly true. Jos Blakeman was no Henry Moore. He sculpted in totally realistic form. In looking at her that way he had been seeing her stripped, imagining the curve of breast and hip molded in clay under his hands. She supposed she should feel flattered that he found her worthy of a second glance in any sphere. Any woman would be. He had sculpted some of the finest female forms of the century.

Those same clever hands were capable of many things, it seemed, considering the uses to which he had put them these last few hours. She had once read somewhere that he refused to have them insured against injury, but there had been no explanation as to why. Jos Blakeman would always have his own very definite ideas on what was and was not necessary, she decided now. This house, for instance. He was a wealthy man who could well afford a custom-built studio anywhere in the world, yet he obviously preferred to make do with what most people would call a comparative hovel miles from any place. It wasn't the first such place he had occupied, she knew. Ben had been lucky in managing to ferret out the location.

They ate from plates perched on their knees, with chairs drawn close to the heater to counteract the rising damp from below. The bread was delicious, crusty and filling the way store-bought stuff never was. Dale followed Jos's example in using the last piece to mop up her plate, happy to ignore convention if he was, too.

"That was really good," she said when the last morsel was gone. "I can't remember when I enjoyed a meal so much!"

"It depends on the degree of need," he rejoined dryly, putting his own plate down on the floor beside his chair. "A crust of bread and a cup of water would taste like nectar to a starving man. The kettle's just about boiling. We'll have some coffee, then you can do the washing up."

Dale smiled, too content at the moment to resent the assumption. "Women's work?" she murmured, and drew a faint lift of the mobile eyebrow.

"Not particularly. Call it a fair division of labor."

"Meaning you'd be willing to take it on if I'd done the cooking?" The warmth was making her drowsy; she could barely keep her eyes open. "Hot water and detergent wouldn't do your hands any good."

In the following small silence she came suddenly wide awake again, realizing what she had said. His expression was enigmatic.

"So you do know who I am."

"I realized in the bath," she said hastily. "I knew the name sounded somehow familiar, but it didn't finally come to me until then."

It was hard to tell whether he believed her or not. Certainly he felt no pleasure in her recognition. "Then you'll understand," he said, "why I don't welcome distraction. We're stuck with the situation and we have to make the best of it until help comes. Just as long as you appreciate that my studio through there is private territory."

Dale gave him an uncertain glance. "You mean I'm not even to be allowed to see any of your work while I'm here?"

His shrug was expressive. "If you had any knowledge of or appreciation for sculpting you'd have recognized the name immediately." There was no hint of pride in his tone, he was simply stating a fact. "I don't see much point."

"I didn't expect to find someone like you here in a place like this," she defended, wishing she had thought of this angle earlier. "If you'd told me your name was Rodin I still wouldn't have associated it with the arts."

His expression didn't change. "You like Rodin's work?"

Honesty, Dale decided, was the best policy—up to a point at least. "To look at and admire. I'm not pretending to have any kind of artistic insight. From what I've seen of yours, I think you were probably influenced by him though."

"And he by Michelangelo." His face had relaxed again. "The maestro himself! Did you ever visit Florence?"

"Once." She smiled. "It was a package tour and we only stayed twenty-four hours."

"Pity. You need to see the galleries with someone who knows what they're talking about—and that doesn't include the average tour guide."

"I realized that before we were halfway through. Luckily we had someone in the group who was able to add a little more detail." The danger moment was past, the door open for a slightly more personalized probing, yet something in her prompted caution. "I'll get the coffee," she said. "Are you going to be doing any more work tonight?"

"If the mood takes me. I sleep in the studio to be on the spot."

Pouring hot water into the coffee mugs, Dale tried to keep her tone casual. "Am I to have the bed in here?"

"Where else?" His tone was dry. "It's the only other room."

She looked up quickly. "There are four doors."

"Two of them leading to the same place. I had the other two bedrooms knocked into one at the same time the roof lights were being installed."

"That's an awful lot of trouble to go to for a house you won't be living in permanently."

Another mistake, but he didn't take her up on it. "It's a good retreat," he said on a mild note. "Always providing the location stays relatively unknown."

That much she could grant him, thought Dale, quelling the sudden urge to tell him the whole truth. She needed this story, if only to give her career a boost. She took the coffee across and held out one of the mugs, meeting the blue eyes with directness. "I won't tell anybody."

The long supple fingers covered hers for a brief moment, their touch sending a sudden quiver running the length of her spine. There was a steellike strength beneath the skin. "I hope I can rely on that," he said softly.

He had released her before she could find breath to reply—if a reply was called for. She moved away from him jerkily, aware of the rapid beat of her heart. Attraction had never happened to her like this before—so swift and flaring. In those few fleeting seconds she had wanted him to reach up and draw her down to him, to feel his lips on hers and hear that deep-timbered voice whispering nameless endearments against her skin. Ridiculous, of course. Should the feeling have been shared she doubted if he would have wasted time on endearments. Where women were concerned his emotions would be purely physical, she was quite certain of that.

She could feel him watching her now, and would have given a lot to know what was in his mind. Had he guessed her feelings? Was he amused by them? Or was he so accustomed to arousing that kind of reaction in the female breast that it no longer meant anything to him at all?

Sitting down, she finished her coffee without looking his way again. Jos was the first to move some few minutes later, getting abruptly to his feet.

"I'm going to work," he announced. "You should find some bedding in the bathroom cupboard. I hope you manage a fairly comfortable night."

He was gone before she could comment. Not that there was much she could have said. The closing of the door along the landing signified failure. She had had her chance and lost it. He would not be coming out of there again before morning, and that might very well be too late.

Washing up the few items they had used didn't take long. Dale stacked everything ready for the morning, then went back to the bathroom to look for the bedding Jos had mentioned. She found sheets and a pillowcase, which together with the blankets already folded at the foot of the bed would suffice. Despite the warmth of the room, the mattress felt cold and damp. She took the precaution of using one of the three blankets under the bottom sheet to stop the cold striking through.

It was past eleven by the time she had finished her preparations. It had stopped raining at last, and the water appeared to have stopped rising, lapping halfway up the fourth riser of the steep staircase. Well over three feet, Dale calculated from the landing, and filthy with it. Imagining the mess after the flood had receded made her shudder. The mud alone would take days to clear.

With all the water below she would have liked to have left the heater on all night, but having little idea of its running capacity and not really trusting herself to refill it, she decided reluctantly that it would be better and safer to turn it off.

With circulation speeded up by the shock of cold sheets against her skin, she found a certain warmth seeping through her within moments. There was little sound from next door; just enough to tell her Jos was still awake if not actually working. Marble and plaster were his favorite mediums, she remembered from her study of his works to date. Two totally different techniques, yet he was at home with either. It had to be the base clay he was working with now. Otherwise she would have heard the sound of the chisel. She wished she could only watch those beautifully shaped and sensitive hands of his at work.

The thought of those hands sent a quiver right through her. If they could transform cold stone into life, what would they do to a living, breathing woman? Jos Blakeman might fight to keep his private life a closed book, but he had been seen with enough different women in tow to have gained something of a reputation. So far there seemed to have been no lasting relationships, which suggested an aversion toward commitment of any kind. He would love them and leave them without a qualm in that arrogant dark head.

Dale had a sneaking suspicion it might even be worth it.

# CHAPTER TWO

SHE AWOKE to early morning light and the sound of running water, the latter, she judged in some relief, emanating from the bathroom. From the window, she looked out on a landscape flooded as far as the eye could see in all directions, with only an occasional ridge of higher ground standing above the water. Perhaps a half mile away on her right rose an embankment that might hold a road but in all probability enclosed the river. The sky above was an overall gray, but higher than yesterday, giving promise of a break perhaps soon to come. It was cool, with the tang of sea air on the light wind. Dale was glad to close the window again and don a light housecoat over her flimsy cotton nightdress.

There was a splashing sound from next door, and a tuneless whistling suddenly cut off as if the perpetrator had just remembered he was not alone in the house. How long he would stay in the bath, Dale had no way of knowing, but it was the only opportunity she was likely to have.

Heart beating fast, she left her room and made her way along the landing to the far door, ignoring the one in between because she had a feeling it might be blocked from the other side. The room was large and L-shaped, with evidence of the renovating still revealed in the roughness of the plastered walls. One whole side of the house had been replaced by framed glass lights extend-

ing into the roof space, admitting a flood of brightness
even on a morning such as this.

The floor immediately beneath was bare of carpeting
and held a sculptor's block set at chest height, its contents covered by a draped cloth. The rest of the room
was sparsely furnished with a divan and a couple of
chairs plus other minor items, the whole set down on a
faded red carpet.

There were some four or five completed works
grouped together on a long trestle at the far end of the
room, one of them a superbly executed figure of a
young girl standing on tiptoe with arms upstretched to
the sky. She was about a third life-size, the tiny breasts
uptilted, a look of wondering anticipation on the face,
which still held a hint of childish roundness in its structure.

If Jos had done this here then he had hardly had access to a model so he must have drawn the figure either
from memory or imagination, Dale realized. Which-
ever, it was a particularly fine example of his work. Jos
Blakeman never exploited the human body, no matter
what the age or sex of his subject. He seemed almost to
revere it, to find beauty even in the imperfect. His
*Mother and Child* showed a woman well past her first
flower, yet the thickened waistline and heavy breasts
served only to emphasize the maturity without in any
way detracting from it.

The other figures were smaller but no less superb.
Dale resisted the urge to pick up and feel the smooth,
flowing lines of a dolphin less than a foot long arched in
joyous flight above a nonexistant sea. Jos Blakeman
didn't often tackle animal subjects, but even the trite
took on new life when breathed upon by the master.

The head of an old man caught her attention next.

This time she just had to stretch out a careful hand to trace the deeply grooved lines in the careworn face. Someone from these parts, she wondered. A fisherman perhaps? There was a lifetime of hard experience etched in that stone.

She was still crouching there in front of it when the door behind her opened again. She came upright slowly, delaying the moment of turning because she knew there was no plausible excuse she could make for being in here at all.

"I'm sorry," she said. "Curiosity got the better of me."

"Not without precedent." His tone was dry but surprisingly lacking in anger. "I should have locked the door."

She came around to face him then, eyes widening a little as they took in the brown muscularity of his body above the towel he had knotted carelessly around his waist. His legs were straight and well shaped and not too hairy, his feet pushed into shabby, leather sandals. There was a hard amusement in the line of his mouth when she finally dragged her gaze back to his face.

"Sorry about the lack of formality," he said. "I'm used to having the place to myself at this hour. Maybe you'd like to be putting the kettle on while I get into some clothes?"

"Yes," Dale said. "Of course."

He made no move away from the door as she approached, forcing her to pass. She did so with head up, hoping that he couldn't hear the thud of her heartbeats. It was ridiculous to allow herself to be affected this way, yet she couldn't help it. Something about this man struck a chord deep inside her.

After putting the kettle on to boil and setting out the

clean mugs ready for the coffee, she made haste to get
washed and dressed herself. Her hair was a mess
because she had gone to bed with it still slightly damp
last night. She smoothed it down with a damp comb,
and contented herself with a token dash of lipstick, feeling that any more elaborate attempt at making up her
face would be somewhat out of place in this setting.

Jos was in the act of pouring hot water into the two
mugs when she went back to the bedroom. He was wearing the same dusty jeans, but the white cotton T-shirt
was clean. Across the front was emblazoned the slogan
Happiness Is, followed by a question mark.

"Supply your own answer," he said, catching her
glance. "It whiles away many an hour."

"Hot coffee on a cold morning," said Dale, taking
the mug from him without lifting her eyes beyond the
level of his chest. "Having a blind eye turned to one's
abuse of hospitality."

The reply came soft. "Who said I'd excused it?
Maybe I'm just biding my time in extracting the ap-
propriate penalty." Blue eyes glinted with mockery as
her head lifted. "Don't give way to impulse if you're going to regret it. It nullifies the whole object."

"All right," Dale said after a moment, "so I don't
regret it. I wanted to see your work, and you obviously
had no intention of showing it to me."

"That was last night. This morning—" he paused and
shrugged "—who knows how I might have felt. How
long were you in there?"

"No more than a few minutes." She was smiling
now, more sure of her ground. "You don't spend long
in the bath."

"I'm essentially a shower man." Another pause while
he remained looking down at her, expression oddly

disturbing, then he said suddenly, "Did you see what I was working on last night?"

Dale shook her head. "I didn't have time. Are you going to show me?"

It was his turn to shake his head. "No," he said on a flat intonation. "And if I catch you taking a look you'll be in trouble."

There was no doubting his seriousness, on that score at least. Dale wondered fleetingly what form that promised trouble might take, and decided it could be worth taking the risk should the opportunity arise. Not that it was likely to do so unless he found some cause to leave the upper floor of the house for any length of time.

"Is the water level dropping yet?" she asked by way of changing the subject, and saw from the faint glint in his eyes that he had a very good idea what she was thinking.

"A few inches perhaps. I told you it was going to take time. Is your aunt likely to be worrying about you?"

Dale only just kept the momentary blankness from showing in her face. A good liar had to have a good memory. How many times had she heard that said?

"I shouldn't imagine so. She isn't expecting me for another couple of days or so." She clamped down hard on the guilt before it could take hold. That was the story she had told, and it was the one she must stick to—for the present, at any rate. There might come a time when she could afford to tell the truth of her being here but that time wasn't yet. When it came—if it came—her senses would tell her.

Meanwhile she took refuge in another tack. "You said something last night about them getting the boats out at times like these. Does that mean we might be rescued?"

"Those that want to be."

"You mean you wouldn't?"

He shrugged. "Why bother?" I've food and fuel for a week or more—even electricity up to now. All I need to withstand a siege."

And his work into the bargain. He needed no more. Dale knew she was going to have to work fast if she was to get anywhere at all. She had no excuse whatsoever for turning down any offer of rescue that did arrive. If it came to that, she wasn't at all sure she would want to turn it down. Jos Blakeman was too disturbing a man with whom to spend too much time alone.

They ate a satisfying and tasty breakfast of fried bacon—rescued from the tabletop refrigerator in the kitchen by Jos in his waders—and more scrambled eggs, helped down with slices of crusty bread. Over a second mug of coffee, Dale managed to steer the conversation back along the lines in which she wanted it to go by remarking that he still hadn't asked her opinion of what she had seen through in the studio.

"Perhaps you're just not interested in any form of criticism," she concluded lightly, and saw his brows lift.

"If you feel qualified to criticize go right ahead," he invited on a sardonic note. "I've had my share."

"Only from those who feel unmitigated praise can't be good for anybody," she came back without hesitation. "And I'm not one of them. I can't make up my mind which piece I like best."

The blue eyes acquired a certain contempt. "They're not designed to be judged in competition with one another. It isn't a dog show!"

"All right," she said placatingly, "so I used the wrong word. I can't decide which moves me more—is that any better?" She didn't wait for any answer. "I think in some ways the old man's head. Is he local?''

He shook his head. "He doesn't exist as far as I'm aware. I don't always need a model.''

"You mean you actually see the shape in your mind?''

"Sometimes. Sometimes I see it in the material itself.'' He was slowly warming to his subject. "Michelangelo said he only released the image already encased in the stone. If you look at his four unfinished *Captives* they all seem to be fighting to free themselves—particularly *Atlas* with his head still encased in the block.''

"Did he deliberately leave them that way, do you think?'' asked Dale, fascinated.

"It's doubtful. Records suggest they were originally intended for Pope Julius's tomb, but the Medici who eventually became Pope Clement wouldn't let him continue so they got put to one side. He may have worked on them from time to time before he finally left Florence. No one knows exactly. When they were found in the house in Via Mozza in fifteen forty-two they were just as they are today—minus a few hundred years.''

Dale brought herself back to the present with a conscious effort. She would have liked to hear more about the great sculptor from one who obviously knew the subject, but it wasn't what all this was about. "When did you first realize you wanted to sculpt?'' she said.

He laughed, "When I was about seven, I think. I lived in North Derbyshire for a time around then. I remember being fascinated by the shapes worn into the granite up on the moors. I thought if wind and rain could do that why couldn't I.''

"But you went for realism rather than abstract.''

"I interpret what I see—or what instinct tells me is there. So does Moore.'' His eyes moved over her, the smile giving way to thoughtfulness. "I'd like to try some preliminary sketches of you while you're here."

"Me?" The word was jerked from her, relaxation flown. "I hardly think. . . ."

"You don't like the idea of taking your clothes off for me?" The smile was back, the mockery pronounced. "I wouldn't touch you, or even come near you; if that's what you're afraid of. All I need is to see you in the flesh."

Dale eyed him squarely. "I thought you said you could work without a model?"

"I don't always have the right one dropped in my lap," he rejoined. "Call it a small return for taking you in, if you like."

She gazed at him for a moment in silence, trying to read the mind behind the blue eyes. Had he guessed? Was this his way of extracting retribution for the deception? It was impossible to tell.

"Why me?" she demanded, taking the bull by the horns. "I don't have anything a thousand other women haven't got, so why me in particular?"

"Because you do have something a thousand other women don't have," he came back on a faint note of impatience. "Your body is unusually well balanced: symmetrical. At least that's how it appears. I can't be certain without seeing you stripped."

"No," she said flatly. She got to her feet, her movements stiff under his gaze. "I'll do the dishes."

Jos put out a hand as she was passing his chair and grasped her wrist. Caught off balance, Dale found herself pulled down into his arms and held there, his face registering the shock in hers with irony. "Is this what you're afraid of?" he asked, and kissed her.

Her own immediate searing response shook her far

more than his action. Instinctively she fought against it, striving to pull clear of the demanding mouth. But he wasn't letting her go that easily. His grasp on her tightened, one hand coming up to hold her head still until she quietened, then sliding on into her hair to find her nape and cradle it.

When he did finally lift his head his breathing rate was scarcely altered, his smile amused as he viewed her flushed face. "You see, they're two separate interests," he said. "If I'd no other interest in you I wouldn't mind indulging this one admittedly. You're not as cool as you act."

"Let me go!" she gritted.

"Certainly." He got up, still holding her, and set her on her feet. "I only wanted to show you I'm perfectly capable of controlling any wild impulses."

*Like Roger*, she thought unsteadily. *Yet not like him, too.* Controlled or not that kiss had triggered a need in her for more of the same.

"I'm not sitting for you," she stated on as firm a note as she could manage. "And there's no way you're going to persuade me!"

She left him standing there and took the used dishes through to the bathroom, running water into the basin with a force that sent it splashing over her sandals. The situation was getting out of hand. She had to get away from this house, this man, as soon as help arrived. But when would that be? Today? Tomorrow? There was no way of knowing. With the water receding so slowly they could be stuck here for heaven only knew how long.

Jos was still in the bedroom when she took the mugs and plates back. He was gazing out through the window, thumbs hooked into the back pockets of his jeans, shoulders blocking the light. There was something about the set of those shoulders that hinted at trouble even before he spoke.

"How long have you been with *World*?" he demanded.

Dale's eyes flew to the bed where her bag rested. It was closed but not in quite the same place. "You've been through my things!" she accused.

"That's right." He swung to face her, expression unnerving. "You ask too many questions for somebody without any vested interest. I felt entitled."

Her chin lifted. "It didn't seem to bother you very much a few minutes ago."

"I was willing to let it pass in return for a little cooperation." The pause was brief. "I still might be."

"Meaning you'd be willing to grant me an interview if I sit for you?" Dale forced a laugh. "I already have enough material for a story thanks!"

He eyed her for a long moment before saying evenly, "I saw a ring in your bag. Does your fiancé have complete faith in you?"

"Of course."

"He knew you were coming here in the hope of cornering me?" His lips twisted at her faint change of expression. "No, obviously not. Maybe he wouldn't have liked the way you planned on doing it. He'd like my version even less."

Dale's throat had gone dry. "What are you getting at?"

"It's simple enough. You publish anything about me without my permission and I'll tell any rival publication interested enough just how you got hold of the information. If this man of yours doesn't object to you going to bed with another man you've nothing to worry about."

The sound in the sky outside had been getting steadily

louder over the last minute or so but it was only now that Dale realized what it was. The helicopter made a pass in line with the window behind Jos's head, coming around to hover while a bullhorn was poked out through a side opening.

"You okay in there?" boomed a hollow-sounding, disembodied voice. "Any assistance needed?"

Jos gave Dale a look that bade her stay exactly where she was, then turned and opened the casement, leaning out and twisting his head up toward the craft.

"No problems," he yelled, cupping his hands around his mouth to carry the sound above the clatter of the rotor blades. "I can last out till the road is clear."

"Understand," came the reply. "Good luck!"

Dale came suddenly out of her stupor as the engine sound increased to lift the hovering craft up and away on a steep cant, diving toward the window with a cry on her lips. Jos caught her by the shoulders and forcibly restrained her, his fingers digging into the bone.

"Too late," he said. "They won't be back. Now, about what we were saying...."

"I won't let you blackmail me!" she flung at him wildly. "Not about anything. I'll tell the whole damned world just what you are!"

"And I'll tell a good section of it just how far a certain journalist was prepared to go to get her story—complete with all the detail the publication I have in mind would want." There was no humor in the taut smile. "You might not be a household name now, but you would be by the time I'd finished with you!"

"I'd sue you for libel," she responded eyes blazing up at him. "You'd have to prove it in court."

"And what a story that would be." He shook his

head. "It wouldn't get that far because you'd never let
it. You'd stand to lose too much."

Dale brought herself sharply under control. "Roger
wouldn't believe it!"

"He'd believe it. Any man who ever kissed you
would probably believe it." His tone mocked her.
"You're what the Americans would call one hot little
number!"

Color flooded her cheeks. "That's not true. I
don't. . . ."

"You don't come on like that for everybody—is that
what you're trying to tell me?" he queried as her voice
trailed away. His gaze dropped to her mouth, expression sardonic. "Let's try it again and see, shall we?"

She tried to twist away from him, but his grasp was
too firm. Drawn up tight against him, she couldn't
escape the descent of his mouth on hers, but she could
and did refuse to submit to it.

With any other man her unyielding rejection might
have been enough. Jos Blakeman was made of sterner
stuff. Despite everything she felt herself beginning to
soften under the determined assault, her senses springing alive to his touch. She couldn't have said the exact
moment at which she stopped resisting and started kissing him back. All she did know was a surging response
that took little account of extraneous detail.

Once again it was Jos who did the drawing back, but
this time with a great deal more reluctance. There was
heat in the blue eyes.

"No use clouding the issue," he said softly. "I've
another use for you, my love." He put his hand under
her chin as she turned her face away, forcing her to look
at him. "Don't be ashamed of a natural instinct. You're
a beautiful, highly sexed, young woman and I'd like

very much to make love to you. Only first I want to sketch you."

"I won't do it," she said, despising herself for what she had just revealed to him. "And we're not going to make love, either."

"Even though you want to."

She drew in a shaky breath. "Even though I want to. I don't know you—don't even like you very much."

"It happens. Women generally don't like admitting it, but sex and love aren't necessarily intermingled." He was still holding her, making her listen to him, his tone matter-of-fact. "You're looking for the kind of satisfaction your senses tell you is possible. Obviously this man you're engaged to isn't supplying it, so ditch him. Shop around a little. Find a man who can match up. Life's too short to lose out on something as vital as fulfillment."

"There are other kinds of fulfillment," she said.

"True. Some are willing to settle for them, too. I doubt if you're one of them."

He paused and smiled a little, eyes moving over her face. "It's a temptation to find out if I could satisfy you."

"You mean you have doubts?"

The irony failed to move him. "Let's say the challenge interests me. We could make a fair exchange. You try to give me what I want and I'll try to do the same for you."

"No thanks." Her lips felt stiff. "If the physical side is really all you think there is to it then you don't have the least conception."

His shrug was philosophical. "So sit for me anyway."

"I said no!"

The blue eyes hardened again suddenly. "It's one or the other. You owe me some kind of return for taking you in."

Dale jerked her head free and moved away from him, striving for a level tone. "I'll give you a check for room and board. That should take care of it."

He let her write the check out, he even took it from her, tearing it in two without bothering to glance at the amount and dropping the pieces on the floor.

"Do that again," he said, "and I'll make the choice for you. You've got till tonight. I can't force you to sit for me without actually tying you down, which rather defeats the object, but I can hold you still for as long as it takes to rouse you past wanting to fight me." He was watching her eyes, his own steely in color. "Who knows, I might even qualify for a bonus."

Dale bit her lip, unable to deny the very probability that he could do exactly as he threatened. Like it or not, he had the power to make her forget all about things like morality and loyalty when he took her in his arms. That he would keep the threat she didn't doubt for a moment. She had tricked her way in here and she was going to pay for it, one way or another.

"You promised me an in-depth interview if I sat for you earlier," she said low toned. "Does the offer still stand?"

"I didn't," he returned, "but I'll accept the condition—with certain reservations."

She drew in a long slow breath. "When do you want to start?"

"Now!" He was moving as he spoke. "Come on through when you're ready. I'll turn the heater up."

She stood for several seconds after he had left the room before moving like a zombie to the bed where she had left the cotton housecoat. She couldn't go through with it, she thought. She really couldn't! Yet what was the alternative? She was trapped in this house with a man who would have no scruples about extracting compensation if she failed to come through on this occasion. What she had to fight was the deep down part of her that would prefer the alternative.

She fought it successfully for long enough to get her out of her things and into the housecoat. All she had left now was the short walk along the landing to the studio, and the initial embarrassment of total nudity. An embarrassment all on her side because Jos certainly wouldn't be feeling any such emotion. He had seen it all before—had sketched and sculpted the female form to an extent where he must be more conversant with it than she was herself. She believed what he had said about the two interests being completely separate. They had to be for the artist in him to take over from the man.

None of it helped. It took everything she had to walk into the studio and meet the unrelenting blue gaze. The divan had been drawn across into the flood of light, a dark blue cover thrown over it. Jos nodded toward it.

"On there. Just try sitting with your legs curled under you to start with." His tone was quite impersonal.

Dale walked over to the divan and stopped, her back toward him. "I can't," she whispered.

"Yes, you can. Don't think about it."

Her fingers fumbled nervously with the tie belt of her housecoat. Still without turning, she let the garment slide swiftly to the floor and put a knee on the divan to sink into the position he had suggested, feeling the warmth surge through her. She could see him out of the corner of her eye sitting on a chair some three yards or so away, a sketching book resting on one raised knee. He studied her narrowly.

"Straighten your back," he said. "And stop trying to hide your breasts. You have a beautiful body. Be proud of it." The pause was brief. "That's better. Now tilt your head forward just a little and lower your eyes. No smile. Just the way you are."

She couldn't see him now without looking up through her eyelashes, and she had a feeling he would notice even that small deviation. The pencil made a faint scratching noise against the paper when he started to sketch. He worked in silence and with total concentration; she could almost feel it emanating from him. If she had wanted to speak she wouldn't have dared.

Over the following minutes she gradually began to forget her self-consciousness, too concerned with the cramp developing in the lower part of her legs. It returned full force, however, the moment Jos got to his feet.

He ignored the jerk of her head, turning up a new sheet as he moved around her. Sculpting was a three-dimensional art, she reminded herself. He needed to view a subject from all angles. All the same it was unnerving. She could feel the hair at the back of her head prickling under his scrutiny.

Her lower leg was quite numb by the time he finally told her to relax. She wanted badly to rub it to return the circulation, but couldn't bring herself to do so under the circumstances.

"Walk around a little if you're feeling stiff," Jos advised casually. He was looking at the sketches not at her, emphasizing a line here and there. "I haven't finished with you yet."

A protest trembled on her lips but remained unspoken. She had come this far, what difference did it make? The quicker he got on with it the sooner it would be over.

He sketched her in several positions altogether; one standing, a couple sitting and one semireclining. By the end of it all there was no embarrassment left, only an aching fatigue. When he finally told her to put on her housecoat she did so without undue haste, rubbing a hand over the back of her neck to ease the crick formed in it.

Jos had his whole attention on the sketches as she left the room. She doubted if he even noticed her going. It wasn't yet midday, she was surprised to note. A week seemed to have passed since she had woken this morning.

After dressing, she heated soup from the stock of tins for lunch, cut hunks of bread to go with it and took the greater part along the landing to knock tentatively on the studio door.

"There's some hot soup here for you," she called.

"Leave it there, I'll get it," came the brusque response.

Dale opened her mouth to warn him it would soon go cold, then closed it again. That was his lookout. She put the tray down near the door and left it there as instructed.

An hour later it still hadn't been taken in, but she refused to go and move it. If he fell over it when he did come out that was also his lookout.

The water appeared to have gone down appreciably, only just lapping the edge of the second tread now. On impulse Dale fetched the waders Jos had used and got into them with a struggle. They were too large both in the feet and the length of the leg, but she managed to fasten them around her somehow.

It felt strange stepping down from the stairs onto the sodden ruin that once had been a carpet. There was a muddy tide mark around the walls some ten or twelve inches above the present level. What furniture was left in the room was obviously ruined, frames already warping, covers dank and discolored. Jos couldn't stay on here in this surely. It would take months to dry the place out.

Not at all sure what aim she had in mind, Dale waded across to the door and dragged it open, almost losing her balance as the dead weight of the sandbags fell inward. The cloud was still high, with patches of blue showing here and there. According to the weather forecast, an improvement that would continue over the coming twenty-four hours.

Because the road was slightly higher than the surrounding fields, her car had its sills almost clear of the water again. The chances of starting the engine were nil, Dale knew, yet something in her prompted a try. It was at least something to do.

She made the vehicle without mishap, opening a door gone stiff on its hinges to reach in and turn the key she had left sitting in the ignition the previous night. There was absolutely no response. Even if the engine was all right, the electrics were useless which amounted to the same thing.

Way back in the middle distance she could see a ridge of slightly higher ground she thought must be the main road—or a better road than the one she was on, at any rate. She could recognize no landmarks from yesterday because there hadn't really been any. If she could reach that she could surely reach the village and secure some help.

*But to what purpose,* she asked herself, standing

there irresolutely. She still hadn't received the promised payment for what she had gone through—and having gone through it surely she wasn't going to leave without it. If it meant spending another night in the house then she could cope. By tomorrow the flood should have receded considerably, making that walk to the village a much more feasible proposition.

She turned to look across at the house standing square and solid on its watery foundations. The studio was at the rear, facing south to gain the maximum light. It gave her a curious sensation to know that Jos Blakeman was locked in there right now studying her nude body from every angle while he planned its transposition into a harder material. If he decided to use her, thousands of other eyes would eventually view her with equal intimacy, yet somehow that failed to bother her. Only Jos would be able to put a face to the body, and that was where the difference lay.

Two successful journeys over the hidden surface of the road had made her careless. Swinging right over the earth bridge toward the house, Dale felt her foot slip over the edge of the ditch and was the next minute up to her waist in water.

Her waders filled immediately, the weight pinning her down like lead-soled diving boots. She was in no danger of drowning, but pulling herself back onto higher ground without help proved impossible, too. In that depth of water, and because of the way she had fastened them, there was no hope of getting them off, either. Panic began to set in as she struggled, lifting her voice in a cry for assistance.

It seemed an age before there was any response. The sight of Jos splashing toward her from the house brought tears of mingled relief and humiliation to her eyes, the latter hardly alleviated by the look on his face.

"Just what are you supposed to be doing?" he demanded, looming over her from the safety of the bank.

"Having a swim," she said furiously. "What kind of an idiot question is that?" She put out a hand toward him. "Just pull me out, will you!"

He stayed where he was looking down on her, brows lifted in the manner she was beginning to recognize. "Ever heard of 'please?'"

"For God's sake—" she began, then stopped and took a hold on herself. She was in no position to argue. "*Please*, will you pull me out," she said in as calm a tone as she could manage. "I have your waders on and they're full of water."

"I gathered that, not being able to find them." He was bending as he spoke, taking her wrists and pulling her back up the side. He started to laugh as he looked at the brimming waders, hastily controlling the impulse when he saw her expression. "We'd better get those off before anything else."

Somehow he managed to unfasten the knotted straps and peel them down, letting out the bulk of the water as he did so. Dale balanced her weight against the bent shoulder while he took each boot off and emptied it, putting each bared foot gingerly down to the concealed surface. Her jeans clung to her legs in wet folds where there was material to spare. For the most part they felt like a second skin.

She made a small sound of protest when Jos swung her up in his arms to carry her to the house, leaving the boots standing.

"I can walk."

"Not in bare feet," he came back. "No knowing what's under all this. I'll come back for the boots."

He took her right into the house, setting her down on the stairs above the water level. "Go and get dried off."

Dale made for the bathroom, squelching at every step. The water had not been clean, and she left a trail of muddy splashes behind her. Stripped, she started the bath running, feeling almost as if the last twenty hours or so had been cancelled out. Almost, but not quite. Too much had happened during that time to be forgotten.

# CHAPTER THREE

SHE HEARD Jos coming up the stairs a moment or two later, but he passed right by the door. He would be going back to the studio, she supposed, to continue the work on which he had been engaged when she called his name. All in all, he had taken the interruption pretty well.

It was simple enough to rinse out her things in the bath when she had finished, and rig the line above it again so that they could drip off. The jeans she had been wearing the previous night were still fairly damp, but she had other clothing in her case. She wrapped the towel around her sarong-style to go through to the other room to find some.

Jos looked up from the little stove where the kettle was just starting to come to the boil. "Coffee?" he asked.

Dale nodded, too nonplussed over finding him there to speak. The towel was large yet in some odd way left her feeling more exposed than she had been earlier.

Jos poured hot water into the two waiting mugs, added milk plus sugar to his own and handed hers black the way she had previously requested it.

"Did you eat?" she asked for want of anything else to say. "I saw the tray was gone."

He moved then, and she saw it sitting there on the floor beside him, the soup congealed in the dish, the bread hardened by long exposure to air.

"I almost fell over it when I heard you yelling," he admitted without any noticeable apology in his tone. "While I'm working I eat when I think about it."

"That can't be very good for your health."

His glance held irony. "I manage."

Dale bit her lip, aware of his meaning. Few men like being told what is good for them; why should she imagine him any different? She changed the subject abruptly. "When am I going to get that interview?"

"Scared I might duck out of my side of the bargain?" he asked. "Don't worry I'll give you the material you're after."

"How do you know what I'm after?" Dale countered. "I could have a totally different angle from the others who've tried to reach you."

He smiled faintly. "A different approach, I'll grant you that." There was a pause, then he shrugged. "Let's get it over. You ask the questions, I'll supply the answers."

"Like this?" She felt color come into her face as she met the blue eyes. "It's hardly the same."

"No," he agreed. "I find that outfit rather more provocative. Get dressed if you want to. I'll wait."

"And watch, too, I suppose!"

"Not if you're self-conscious about it. There's always the bathroom."

He was mocking her, and they both knew it. Dale put down her coffee mug with care and went to open her suitcase, extracting the only dry clothes she had left. She hadn't anticipated an extended stay.

The already small bathroom was made even smaller by the line of drying clothing. Dale cursed under her breath when she put a finger through her stockings as she was pulling them on. Luckily the hole was near the top and the skirt of her dress was mid calf, so it was hardly likely to be noticed. Not that it mattered so much anyway. She was of no further interest to Jos Blakeman now that he had what he wanted.

He eyed the plain, cream-colored dress with scant approval when she went back to where he sat.

"Not your color," he commented. "Doesn't do a thing for you."

Dale ignored him, fetching her notebook and pencil from her bag and coming back to finish off the lukewarm coffee before sitting down in the chair opposite him.

"You said you were around seven when you first became interested in sculpture as an art," she began, noting down the fact. "How old were you when you sculpted your first female form?"

"Eight," he said promptly, and laughed at the look on her face. "True enough. I had a Labrador bitch. I used to model her in Plasticine."

Dale's smile was reluctant. "You know what I meant."

"All right, I was around twenty—although I'd painted a few before that. There was a time when I considered sticking with a brush in preference, but I missed that third dimension. And women in particular?" He paused and shrugged. "Perhaps initially I was just indulging a natural leaning. All my subjects tended to be young and beautiful. It took me a long time to realize it was the anatomical structure that fascinated me more than the outer covering—so far as sculpting was concerned anyway."

Dale couldn't bring herself to look up. "Where did you move to when you left Derbyshire?" she asked obliquely.

"Hampshire." His tone had shortened.

"Are your parents still alive?"

"No."

It was harder work even than she had anticipated. Over the following twenty minutes or so, she only managed to build up a sketchy, unsatisfying picture of this unapproachable man. When she asked why at thirty-five he still wasn't married he showed every sign of reaching the end of his tolerance.

"Because I'll give no woman the right to take part of my income away from me anytime she feels like finishing it," he said bluntly.

"That happened to someone you know?" Dale ventured.

"More than one." He shook his head. "You're a faithless sex."

"Not all of us," she protested.

"No?" There was a wealth of irony in the word. "Are you going to tell your fiancé about all this?"

Dale hesitated, aware of the trap. "It's not the same thing," she said at last. "I haven't been unfaithful to him."

"You've wanted to be. You admitted as much. And you were scared enough of putting yourself to the test to accept the alternative."

"It was the only way of getting you to talk to me."

"Which means you put your job before his feelings for starters."

"Why not?" she burst out, incensed. "He puts his before me!"

His lips twisted. "On a par perhaps, but it's all or nothing with most of you. What does he do exactly?"

"He's with a firm of diamond merchants," she said after a moment. "Hatton Gardens."

"Big league."

"There's more to it than that!"

"Meaning you'd love him just as much if he were a truck driver."

"No, that isn't what I meant. He's temperamentally suited to the job he does. If he drove a truck he wouldn't be the same kind of man at all. On the other hand, that doesn't mean I couldn't love a truck driver."

"Oh, I'm sure you could." His tone was bland. "Just for different reasons."

"You're suggesting I'm only interested in his position?"

The blue eyes were very direct. "Are you?"

Dale couldn't hold his gaze for long. "I thought I was supposed to be doing the interview," she said stiffly.

"So you are." He paused before adding on a level note, "Not very comfortable having your private life put under a microscope, is it?"

"It's my job," she defended.

"And we struck a bargain." His shrug was eloquent. "So get on with it."

Dale didn't because she found she couldn't. Her well of questions seemed to have dried up. "I think I have enough," she said after a moment or two, still not meeting his eyes. "It's going to take me some time to sort this lot out."

"Then you won't object if I get on with some work."

He was getting up as he spoke, heading for the door. Dale waited until he had reached it before saying tentatively, "When am I going to get away from here?"

"Tomorrow, all being well."

"Not before then?"

He turned to look at her, brows lifting with unconcealed sarcasm. "If you fancy a long swim. The road should be almost cleared by morning. It won't be a pleasant trip but it should be possible to make the village. That should have cleared even quicker as it's on higher ground. In the meantime you're just going to have to reconcile yourself to spending another night on the bed over there. It wasn't that uncomfortable, was it?''

Dale shook her head in reluctant acknowledgement. "No, but I'm due back in London tomorrow."

"And your fiancé is going to start questioning your whereabouts if you aren't." It was more statement than question. "Where does he *think* you are?"

"He's away himself," she admitted. "He doesn't know about this job at all."

Jos considered her thoughtfully. "He'll have to know when the article comes out—or doesn't he bother reading your stuff?''

"Not always." Her head was held high. "In any case, he doesn't have to know how and when."

"So you're not planning on telling the world how we were marooned here together."

"No." The denial came out more forcibly than she had intended, drawing a faint smile to his lips.

"Pity. I was looking forward to reading about it myself. Don't forget I want to see a draft before you publish anything."

"There was no such agreement!"

"I said with certain reservations. I don't like being misquoted. Between us we should be able to hammer out a reasonable account."

Dale hadn't moved from her chair. Now she said tautly, "How am I supposed to get a copy to you?"

"There's the mail."

"That could take a week or more."

"Then it will have to take a week or more." His tone

was adamant. "I want to see that copy first, do you understand?"

There was little else Dale could do for the moment but agree, although she did so with reservations of her own. Jos had given his consent to the interview without mention of any such condition and that, as far as she was concerned, let her off the hook. What she intended writing about him was only what he himself had told her, and he could hardly quarrel with that.

She found the afternoon dragging by on leaden wings. At one point she heard the helicopter, or a similar one, and saw it flying eastward from the window, but it was too high and too far away from her to attract the pilot's attention.

How would she explain her presence here anyway? she asked herself resignedly. It would be difficult without going into detail, and these things had a way of getting passed on. She had not told Ben Reynolds just how she intended going about the task he had set her, so let him think she had approached it in the conventional way and become trapped in the village. These last two days were between her and Jos Blakeman, and they were going to stay that way.

Jos emerged briefly from the studio to eat a scanty meal at six-thirty, vanishing again with scarcely a word spoken between them. Washing the dishes in the bathroom, Dale could still feel the impact of his gaze on her. She had been certain he was going to ask her to sit for him again, and had spent the whole time nerving herself for a flat refusal. Once was more than enough. His failure to do so had been something of an anticlimax. She would have given a great deal to know just what had been going on behind those enigmatic blue eyes.

If it had been a long afternoon, it proved to be an

even longer evening. There were some paperback books piled on a stool at the back of the bedroom. Dale browsed through them but found nothing to suit her taste. She doubted if they belonged to Jos at all—unless he read thrillers for light relaxation, and somehow she couldn't see it.

Nothing about this place really fitted him. It was somewhere quiet and away from it all to work, that was all. His main place of residence was in the Thames's valley, an address too easily accessible for solitude. With his third one-man show coming up in a few weeks' time, it wouldn't be long before he returned there. The way things were here he might even decide to do so immediately. The downstairs' rooms were uninhabitable until they had dried out, and that could take weeks.

As far as Dale knew, no one had ever seen the studio at Teddington. If she could only persuade Jos to allow her to be the first—even perhaps get a photographer along. If he did ask her to sit for him again she might agree on that condition. After all, having done it once what was there left to be afraid of?

The headache that had been hovering all afternoon developed slowly over the following couple of hours into a steady throb right behind her eyes, making her feel slightly sick. By ten o'clock her limbs were aching. She found aspirin in the bathroom cabinet and washed three of them down with water, relieving the symptoms at least. Being ill in this place would be no picnic, she thought, shivering as she prepared for bed. She had to get away tomorrow.

The aspirins soothed her into a fitful doze. Awakening sometime later, she found Jos sitting on the edge of the bed with a hand to her forehead.

"I heard you muttering in your sleep as I crossed the

landing," he said. "You sounded feverish. Do you feel hot?"

Dale shook her head, and wished she hadn't as pain lanced through it. "No, I feel cold," she got out. A shiver ran through her as if to confirm the statement. "Are there any more blankets?"

"Only the ones on the divan." His hand was still across her forehead. "Your skin is burning. I'd say you'd got a chill." He took the hand away and ran it under the covers where she was lying. "This mattress feels damp. Why didn't you say? We could have dried it off in front of the heater."

"It didn't seem that bad. I put a blanket under the sheet last night." Dale shivered again, unable to control it. "I haven't sneezed or anything."

"I said a chill not a cold. It's a different thing." He paused, eyeing her in the semidarkness. "All I have in the house is aspirin."

"I know," she said. "I took some earlier."

"How much earlier?"

"Ten o'clock."

"It's past two now, so you could have some more." He stood up purposefully. "Warmth is the main thing."

Dale protested weakly as he bent and scooped her up bodily, top blankets and all. "What are you doing?"

"Taking you through to the studio," he said. "It's warmer than this, and drier. I've had the heater on right through."

His arms themselves were warm, and comforting. "I can't take your bed," she said. "Where are you going to sleep?"

"With you," he came back levelly, and carried her from the room.

The divan covers were turned back, proving he had

been to bed that night. The electric light had been turned off, but the moonlight flooding in through the vast expanse of glass provided more than enough illumination. Set on her feet, Dale hugged the blankets closer around her as she watched him pull back his own to reveal spotless white sheets.

"Get in," he said. "I'll fetch the aspirin. They might help."

Dale stayed where she was, looking up at him with darkened eyes. "Were you serious just now?" she forced herself to ask.

His smile was fleeting. "Very. It's the best way I can think of of warming you through again quickly. It won't cure you, but it might stop the worst of it." His voice firmed when she still failed to make the move. "Look, I'm not going to be making any passes at an invalid. I'm concerned about having you really ill while we're still stuck here. If you don't trust me, that's too bad. Now get into bed."

She did so with reluctance, relinquishing her hold on the blankets to draw the others over her. The shivering wouldn't stop, try as she might to control it. Feeling like this, the last thing she wanted was any man's arms around her, but it seemed she was to have no choice in the matter. She only hoped Jos was a man of his word.

He came back with the aspirin and a glass of water, and made her sit up to take them. Lying down again on her side, Dale could hear him moving around out of her range of vision. There was a cold draft of air when he lifted the bedclothes on the far side of the divan, then the weight of his body was descending behind her, his arm curving around her waist to pull her to him.

"Relax," he said against her hair. "Remember what we talked about this morning."

The shiver running through her now had a different quality. "When this morning?" she asked huskily, and felt his hand press her midriff.

"You know what I mean. Just go to sleep."

Dale couldn't do that. Even when warmth began seeping through her the tension refused to give. The legs tucked in behind hers were clad in what felt like thin cotton but his arms and chest were bare. She could feel the hardness of the latter against her shoulder blades, the tickle of hair. Roger had never known the intimacy of holding her this way in the night. How would he feel if he could see her now? Certainly he'd never believe there was no emotion involved.

Dale didn't believe it herself. She could feel it rising inside her like the flood tide. Not merely physical; there was more to it than that. But how much more? It was impossible to fall in love with a man one had known only a matter of hours—wasn't it?

"Who are you most afraid of?" Jos asked softly into the silence. "Me or yourself?" He answered the question for her when she remained silent. "You're in no fit state for what you think I have in mind. Even if you were I'd think twice before making that kind of commitment."

"What kind of commitment?" The words were dragged from her.

"You're no one-night stand. If I once made love to you I'd want to do it again. I got involved once before and it didn't work out. I'm not sure I want to risk it a second time."

Dale was very still, her breathing ragged and shallow. "You're taking rather a lot for granted," was all she could find to say.

"No, I'm not. You know how it could be between us.

You've known since last night. It happens like that sometimes. Total and mutual attraction." His voice was very quiet, almost hypnotic in quality. "I've never met this fiancé of yours, but I doubt if he's capable of giving you what you need from a man."

"While you are."

"I'd say so."

Then do it, she wanted to say. Make love to me, Jos. It was only the thought of the morning and the inevitable regrets that kept her from abandoning herself to the need. She owed Roger better than that.

"I want to go back to the other room," she got out. "I can sleep in a chair."

"And finish up with pneumonia." His hold on her tightened. "You're in no danger. I just told you why, I want you away from here tomorrow."

No more than she wanted to go, Dale told herself with emphasis. Involvement with Jos Blakeman could only bring ultimate heartache. Wonderful while it lasted maybe, but devastating when it finished, as it certainly would. She wasn't cut out for that kind of relationship. She didn't think she ever could be. Yet could she go back to Roger knowing how much was missing from theirs.

She must have slept eventually because when she opened her eyes again it was morning, the pale light flooding the room. Sometime during the night she must have turned onto her back, lying now close up against Jos's side with his arm heavy across her breasts. When she turned her head she saw he was already awake and watching her, his face bare inches from hers.

For a moment or two they were both of them still, eyes level. For Dale it was like looking into fathomless pools; she felt herself drowning in them, heard the drumming of her heart in her ears. When he moved his hand slowly down to cover her breast it was what she wanted, too. She met his lips halfway.

The world caught up with her as he began to remove her nightdress, Roger's image springing in her mind. What she had refused him she was on the verge of giving to a stranger—a man who felt nothing for her beyond this one basic desire. She clutched at the lean brown hands, staying their movements.

"No," she said painfully. "Don't, Jos!"

His jaw contracted but he didn't attempt to fight her. "Why?" he asked. "Why the change of mind?"

"I'm not free. I can't go back to Roger this way."

"Then don't go back to Roger," he said. "Come with me instead."

She stared up at him with darkened eyes, trying to read the mind behind those looking back at her. "Where?"

"Home. My home. I'll be leaving here myself just as soon as I can arrange to have my gear collected." One hand lifted to cup her cheek, the thumb moving slowly and sensuously across her lips. "I want you to stay with me, Dale. I thought I could let you walk away from me, but I can't."

It was difficult to say it. "For how long?"

"As long as it lasts. Who knows."

"And after?"

His expression altered a little. "We'd both be free agents. That goes without saying."

She had expected nothing else but it still hurt. "Why me?" she asked on a low note. "You can't be short of that kind of companionship."

"What I need I can generally find," he agreed without particular inflection. "We're not talking about an occasional relationship. I want you because you're unlike any other woman I know—because you have something I need right now."

"Like a body?"

He smiled at the cynicism, sliding his hand down over her to come to rest lightly against her thigh. "Not just any body. This one is special. I know it already in my mind—every curve, every line, every beautiful inch of it. I want to make it mine in every possible sense of the word. I want to own you, Dale."

"Until you find some other interest." She shook her head, throat aching. "I don't want to be owned. Not by you or anybody. Let's just forget the whole thing, shall we?"

He didn't move, looking down at her with a spark in his eyes. "I could take you right now."

"You could," she agreed, trying to sound sure of herself, "but you wouldn't get any satisfaction out of it. I'd make sure you didn't."

There was a moment when she thought she might have failed to convince him, then the spark slowly faded.

"All right, so that's not the way I want it, either. But we're not going to forget it. You're coming back to London with me."

"No." She said it with all the firmness she could muster. "I'm going back to Roger."

"And security?"

"Don't sneer at security. It has a lot going for it."

"Not enough to make you happy."

"Do you think what you're offering does?"

His lips widened mirthlessly. "I suppose you might consider it if I asked you to marry me."

"No," she denied, "I wouldn't. Marriage isn't something I'd ever step into just for the sake of acquiring a husband.''

''Then come and live with me.''

''Not on your terms.''

There was an ominous quality to the sudden set of his mouth. ''I'm going to have you,'' he said. ''On any terms. Not now. You were right about that. The satisfaction would be too short-lived. I'll get a great deal more out of taking you away from your precious Roger!''

He rolled away from her before she could find any response, throwing back the covers to slide from the bed and stand up. Dale turned her back on him as he reached for the clothing he had flung over a nearby chair, lying there rigidly until he came into view on his way to the door. He was wearing the jeans but carrying his shirt in his hand. She knew he wouldn't have turned a hair had she watched him dress.

The threat he had made worried her more than a little. If he told Roger she had slept with him it would only be the truth, and nobody was going to believe nothing else had happened. That he could find her fiancé she didn't doubt for a moment. She had given him enough information to make that relatively easy. Yet what would it gain him? She was hardly going to turn to him afterward.

Or was she? Dale wished she could be sure of her own strength of mind. Jos Blakeman exercised an undeniable power over her. If he really set out to get what he wanted would she have the will to resist him? Would she even want to resist him when it came right down to it?

She was sitting on the edge of the bed with the sheet wrapped around her when he came back from the bathroom.

"The level's down but the road isn't completely clear yet," he announced in matter-of-fact tones. "Might take another twenty-four hours."

"I'm leaving today—this morning," Dale came back firmly. "I don't care if I have to paddle to dry land!"

"Another soaking isn't going to do you any good."

*Staying on here won't, either,* she thought. Aloud she said, "I feel perfectly all right thanks. I'm not hot or shivering."

"I must have misread the symptoms." He eyed her for a brief moment, then shrugged. "If that's what you want. I'll get you as far as the village and see about having your car towed in. Rented, is it?"

Dale nodded, nonplussed by the change in him. "Have you any idea how long it might take a garage to fix it up ready to drive again?" she asked, striving for the same attitude.

"Depends how far the damp has penetrated the cables, I'd imagine. With heat on them, I'd say no less than twenty-four hours. Best thing you can do is leave it and go back by train. The insurance should cover collection as well as the cost of repairs. There's a line from Spalding." His smile held irony. "You might even get to see the tulips after all."

Her eyes were on the covered workstand, assessing the shape beneath without reaching any definite conclusion. She wanted to ask what he had been working on but didn't dare. It was doubtful if he would tell her anyway.

"I won't have time," she said. "I must get back today. I hope it's going to be possible to reach Spalding from the village."

"That's something you're going to have to find out. The main roads should be okay. There's a local news bulletin in half an hour. We'll know conditions better then. I'll get breakfast started while you dress."

"Jos." Her voice was low. "What you said...."

"There's nothing to talk about." His tone was perfectly steady. "Why don't you go and get your things."

It was all she was going to get out of him, that was for certain. Dale was left with a sudden sense of anticlimax. He hadn't meant what he had said, of course. He had merely been angered by her refusal of an invitation many would no doubt have been only too glad to accept. There would be no follow-through. He would simply write her off.

# CHAPTER FOUR

THE BULLETIN gave an encouraging report. Apparently all main roads in the area were open, and emergency restrictions lifted. Once they reached the village it should be possible to get transport direct through to Spalding on the A16. After that, it depended on the trains. With any luck Dale hoped she might make London before evening.

The shoes she had arrived in were dry if somewhat stiff. She got them on with a struggle, planning to discard them as soon as she reached a place where she could change. Her slacks she rolled above the knee, trusting they would not be ploughing through any water deep enough to reach them. An hour should see them through the worst.

Similarly attired, Jos hoisted her overnight case and led the way downstairs. He had already brushed out some of the muddy residue from the ground floor, leaving an oozing path through to the door. Outside, the fields were still submerged, but the lane itself was only a few inches deep in water. He set off with caution in the general direction of the road, probing ahead on occasion with a stick he was carrying for the purpose.

Long before they eventually reached it, it was possible to see occasional traffic moving in both directions along the road. Emerging at last from the lower level, Dale gave a sigh of relief. The rest should be comparatively simple now.

"I can manage from here, I think," she offered tentatively when they stopped to change footwear at the roadside. "You'll have a lot to do back there."

"I'm not stopping," he said. "I told you that. I've things to arrange for myself as well as you." He stood up, swinging the dripping sneakers by their tied laces from a finger. "Let's move."

Dale rolled down her trouser legs and hastened to follow him, carrying her own ruined shoes in a similar fashion until she could find somewhere to dump them. Despite all caution, the bottoms of her slacks had managed to get splashed. They would have to dry on her unless she found somewhere to change her clothing. Not that she had much of a choice. Her jeans were still damp from yesterday's episode, which left only the cream dress, and after what Jos had said about that she felt she would rather put up with wet trouser bottoms for a while.

They reached the village around eleven, found the local garage willing to see to Dale's car, although she was unable to extract a firm promise as to when.

"Got a lot on," advised the mechanic. "Came through the bottom like a millrace it did. Still sweeping out down at lower end. Talk about a mess!"

In the end he took the name and address of the rental company and promised to let them know when the vehicle was available for inspection. In the meantime he advised her to contact the company herself as soon as she could.

"I suppose I should do it from here," Dale said reflectively as they came away from the garage. "They're expecting it back this afternoon."

"Use the pub phone," Jos said, nodding across the road. "I could use a drink. I'll check on times of buses into Spalding, too, while you're doing it."

It took Dale little more than ten minutes to complete the call. She found Jos in the lounge when she finished. He was halfway down a pint of lager, and had the gin and orange she had requested waiting for her. He lifted an eyebrow inquiringly as she sat down at the table under the window.

"Everything settled?"

"Not to their satisfaction," she acknowledged ruefully. "They wanted me to wait till the car was dried out and drive it back myself."

"Might not be possible anyway if the coil's had it. Ignore them. You've done all that's required in contacting them. I suppose the magazine paid for the rental."

"Yes."

"Then if there are any comebacks at all it's their pigeon. Have your drink. There's a bus at twelve-twenty, so I've ordered lunch here first. It might be the only meal you get before you reach home." The pause was scarcely noticeable. "Where is home, by the way?"

"Potter's Hill," she responded vaguely. "I have an apartment."

"Sharing?"

She shook her head. "I tried it to start with but it didn't work out. Living with someone else isn't easy." She caught his eye and felt her expression stiffen despite herself. He would think she had said that deliberately.

It was difficult to tell what he was thinking. "It has to depend on the people concerned," was all he said. "I ordered the roast beef and Yorkshire with all the trimmings by the way. After two days on makeshift meals I think we both deserve it."

"I'm surprised they're organized enough to put on a meal like that," Dale commented, only too glad to change the subject. "I expected complete chaos."

"The water didn't get up this end, and they're well used to carrying on in these parts."

There was silence for several minutes after that. There were only two other people in the bar, both obviously regulars from the way the barmaid had greeted them. Dale looked around at the oak beams and horse brasses, the big stone fireplace with its obligatory copper kettle and fire irons, the red Axminster carpet and green velvet upholstery. When she finally came back to the man opposite, he was leaning with both elbows on the table and looking into the lager glass with a faint smile on his lips. She would have given a great deal to know what he found amusing.

"How long do you expect to be before you can get away?" she asked.

His head came up slowly, the blue eyes too knowledgeable for comfort. "A day or two."

"And you'll not be coming back?"

"It's doubtful." His shoulders lifted. "I planned to make it a regular retreat, but it hasn't worked out that way."

"If you mean because the secret is out, I won't make it public," Dale assured him. "I already promised you that."

"I know you did. It wasn't what I meant." He looked at her for a moment. "I still meant what I said about the article before you publish though."

"If you're going to be back in London that won't be so difficult," she agreed. "Ben might decide to put it into next month's edition and hold something else over." She laughed. "I hope you won't go and give anyone else the same material. I'd hate to get pipped at the post with a scoop!"

His return smile was dry. "I doubt if anyone else could supply quite the same brand of persuasion."

The laughter faded as another more desperate emotion suddenly swamped her. Take me back with you, she wanted to beg him. Keep me here. She looked away swiftly, afraid he might see too much. It was no use wishing. It couldn't work out. Not on the terms he had offered. It would be like living on a tightrope, never knowing when the end was going to come. She was better off with Roger.

The lunch was excellent but Dale found herself unable to eat more than a portion of it. Afterward there was just time to have coffee before they made their way outside to the bus stop some hundred yards down the street.

"You should get a connection in Peterborough," said Jos as they tagged on behind the line of about five people. "Here's the bus now."

He saw her right to the doors before handing over her case, standing back immediately with a brief nod of his head. The last Dale saw of him was a lean figure striding off along the street. He didn't look around as the bus passed him.

It was after eight-thirty when Dale finally reached the converted Victorian house where she lived. Going wearily up the stairs, she was almost knocked over by the hurried descent of the second-floor tenant.

"Sorry," proffered the other, grabbing the handrail to aid her passing. "I'm late for a date.... By the way," she tossed over her shoulder, "Your phone's been ringing on and off for the last half hour."

Roger, of course. The arrangement had been that he would phone her when he got back. Right then all Dale wanted was a hot bath and bed, but there was no chance of that.

She let herself into the apartment with her key and dropped the case onto the floor in the tiny hallway before pushing open the door to the sitting room. It was odd how strange the place looked after only a few days away from it. After the house in the fens it seemed almost too neat and tidy. Sitting down on the settee, she dialed Roger's number, steeling herself for the explanations that were bound to follow.

His voice when he answered sounded disturbingly unfamiliar. She had grown accustomed to a deeper, more modulated tone, a certain inflection. Fleetingly she wondered what Jos was doing right this moment.

"Roger, it's me," she said. "I just got in."

"I haven't been back all that long myself," he said. "Had some delay on the flight." There was a pause and a slight change of tone. "Where were you? I've been calling for nearly an hour."

It was only then that Dale realized she wasn't going to tell him anything about the past three days. As far as he knew she had been right here in London. Why complicate matters?

"I went out for a meal," she said quickly. "I wasn't sure if you'd be back tonight, and I didn't feel like cooking for myself. Have you eaten?"

"No, I haven't." It was said on a distinctly plaintive note. "I thought we might eat out together, but if you've already had dinner...."

Dale thought briefly and longingly of bed and sleep then dismissed both from her mind. "There's steak in the fridge," she offered with resignation. "I could have a grill ready by the time you get here."

"That sounds good," he agreed as she had known he would. "I'll be with you in half an hour."

Showered and changed, Dale felt a little more human,

if still not exactly eager and agog to see her fiancé. She found sausages, mushrooms and tomatoes to go with the steak, and arranged the lot under the electric grill. Roger's appetite was unpredictable. What he didn't want she could always throw away. Inevitably she was reminded of the last time she had cooked for a man. Jos would be doing it for himself now—if he bothered. He shouldn't neglect himself that way when he was working. Eventually it would start to tell on his health.

She had to stop thinking about Jos Blakeman, she told herself desperately at that point. She had had her chance to stay with him, and she had turned it down. Quite rightly so, too. She was going to marry Roger, a man she both knew and trusted. What Jos had been offering was only a minor part of any relationship—or should be. And who was to know whether she might not find an equal fulfillment with Roger if she stopped holding back herself. Perhaps he too needed reassurance before he fully let himself go.

His kiss when he did arrive was certainly warm enough. "I've missed you," he said, holding her face between his hands to look at her. Then on a faint note of criticism, "You look tired, darling. What have you been doing with yourself?"

"Just working," she said, and drew away from him. "Dinner is almost ready. Why don't you fix us both a drink while I see to the steak."

"Good idea." He moved across to the wall cabinet where she kept both bottles and glasses. "Usual for you?"

"Please." Dale was glad to escape into the kitchen area, cut off from the rest of the room by a sliding partition. She had already set the table, and Roger liked his steak rare so that wasn't going to take long. Perhaps if she opened a bottle of wine and lighted candles her mood would come right. It had to. Tonight she was going to go as far as Roger wanted. They were engaged to be married. Why should he have to wait any longer? Why should she, if it came to that? She needed to know how it would be between them. She needed very much to know.

The partition was opened far enough for her to see through to where he stood pouring the drinks. At six feet, he was roughly the same height as Jos, though not quite as broad in the shoulders and somewhat heavier around the middle. In looks he had the actual advantage, yet those handsome, clean-cut features and the stylish fair hair tonight failed to stir the same kind of admiration. Another, more angular face kept getting in the way, mouth lifted in that sardonic fashion, dark hair falling in a thick, uncontrollable comma across the forehead. Forget Jos she told herself forcibly. Roger loved her in addition to wanting her. What more could she ask?

The wine and the candlelight helped her relax while she watched Roger eat. He talked about his trip for the greater part of the meal, saving her the trouble of making conversation for the sake of it. While the coffee was perking, she went through to the bedroom and put on a silky little housecoat she had bought a couple of weeks back and never worn before. It was the leisure type, with tiny buttons down to the waist and a softly falling skirt in a deep gold color striped in a paler shade. His eyes lighted up appreciatively when she went back to where he sat waiting for his coffee.

"I like that," he said. "New isn't it? Gold suits you. It brings out your hair."

Dale found herself trembling a little as she filled the

cups. Nerves, she thought. She was planning what should be a purely spontaneous decision. It would be all right, she assured herself, once Roger started making love to her. She would let him take over then, leave all decisions in his hands. By this time tomorrow she would be laughing at the thought that Jos Blakeman could ever have threatened to come between them.

It was Roger who made the first move, seizing hold of her hand as she straightened from pouring more coffee, and patting the cushion at his side with a little smile on his face.

"Put that down," he said softly, "and come and sit here with me. I haven't had a chance to kiss you properly yet."

Dale obeyed without argument, sliding her arms around his neck and abandoning herself to the kiss with an almost feverish desire. When he lifted his head his eyes held a curious expression.

"I should go away more often," he murmured. "Have you missed me so much, Dale?"

"Yes," the whisper was fierce. "Don't talk, Roger. Just go on kissing me!"

He pulled her across him to cradle her head against his shoulder while he did so, his fingers easing open the buttons on her housecoat to slide inside in a caress that did little to arouse her. Dale clung to him, desperate to feel that same vital spark she had known with Jos. It had to be there, somewhere. This was the man she was going to marry. Of course she wanted him. She *had* to want him.

Whatever the lack in her emotions it obviously did not communicate itself to Roger. His hands were possessive.

"I've never known you quite like this before," he said

with his lips against her throat. "Dale, you can't send me away tonight. I want to make love to you, darling—all the way. It's what you want, too, isn't it?"

"Yes. No!" She pushed him suddenly away, sitting upright with a jerk, the tightness in her chest matched only by that in her throat. "Roger, I'm sorry, I just can't."

"Don't be a goose," he admonished with tolerant indulgence. "Of course you can. What's to stop you?" He pulled her down again, holding her to him with desire in his eyes. "We're going to be married. Why hold back any longer?"

"Why did you?" she asked on a low husky note. "If you really thought that's what I wanted, why didn't you just pick me up and take me to bed?"

"Because it isn't my way," he said, smiling a little. "I'm not the Tarzan type, darling. You must know that. It has to be your decision as well as mine."

"Then my decision is no."

His brows came together. "I don't understand you. Were you deliberately teasing me?"

"No. No, of course not." She searched her mind for some explanation—*any* explanation. "I thought I could, then found I couldn't," was all she came up with. "I'm sorry, Roger."

"So you keep saying." Sighing he took her legs and swiveled them across to put her once again onto the sofa. "I think the sooner we get married the better, don't you? We don't have any reason to wait."

She had to say something, and this was not the time to be making anymore meaningful decisions. "Yes," she murmured.

"So say when."

"You'll have to give me time to get things arranged,"

she said hurriedly. "My father is going to insist on a white wedding in the parish church, with all the trimmings to follow. He likes to do everything right."

"Well, there's nothing wrong in that. I can appreciate he'd want to give his only daughter a big send-off." He leaned forward and kissed the tip of her nose. "You can talk to the parents this weekend while we're there—start the ball rolling, so to speak. Afraid I won't be able to get away before Saturday morning though. I've an unbreakable appointment tomorrow night. Why don't you go down by train and I'll join you. It will give you a chance to sort out dates, et cetera."

"I might do that." Dale felt trapped. This was all her fault. She had sparked things off. Yet wasn't it the best thing that could happen? Once married to Roger she could forget there had ever been a man called Jos Blakeman—at least so far as she personally was concerned.

BEN REYNOLDS greeted her return next morning with a gratifying relief.

"I was beginning to wonder if you'd come to any harm up there," he confessed. "Bad, was it?"

"Bad enough," Dale agreed, hoping he wasn't going to ask too many questions. "I had to abandon the car and come back by train in the end. The rental company isn't too thrilled about it."

"Shouldn't imagine they are." The comment held little concern for rental companies. He viewed her shrewdly. "Guess you didn't get what you went after."

"As a matter of fact, I did." Dale was hard put to keep the same level tone as she held up her notebook. "It's all in here. I thought I'd make a start on the write-up this morning."

"The sooner the better." Ben looked as near nonplussed as he was ever likely to get. "He actually consented to an interview?"

"Quite a lengthy one," Dale returned with her fingers crossed behind her back. "Background detail, the lot. It should stretch to a full-page spread."

"More, if we use photographs. Pity you didn't have a photographer along. A shot of him actually at work would have put the jam on the bread."

"I don't think he would have agreed to that," said Dale and saw the bushy, graying brows lift."

"You got to know him pretty well in—how long were you actually with him?"

There it was: the question she had been dreading. She could have lied about it, but she could see the pitfalls in that, too. Anyway, why bother? Ben didn't know Roger, and was hardly likely to give her away if he was to meet him.

"Two days," she said. "At least, one full day and two nights, to be exact." (Was it really only that?) "I got caught in the floods. I only just managed to reach the house."

"Good timing." It was said with irony. "He could hardly turn you away in those conditions. Did you tell him why you were there?"

"Not right away. He found out."

"Dangerous. Going by past performances you could have found yourself up to your neck in it with a vengeance. Or have reports been exaggerated some?"

Catching his eye, Dale found herself flushing a little. "I can't say about other times. He was angry at first, but he cooled down when I promised not to reveal his whereabouts to every Tom, Dick and Harry. He also wanted an assurance that he'd have the chance to see the article before it went into print. Naturally I gave it to him."

"Naturally." Ben looked disgruntled now. "Are we supposed to send it to him, or what?"

"He's coming back to London in a couple of days," she told him. "Someone can take it out to Teddington and get his approval on the spot."

"It's your pigeon. You take it out and make it as soon as possible. I want it in next month's issue." He paused there, expression difficult to define. "Congratulations anyway. It's a first-class scoop. The kind of stuff that guy turns out makes him front-page interest to Joe public."

His tone brought a spark to her eyes. "The kind of stuff he does turn out has a whole lot more to it than a quick line in titillation!"

"So what if it does? I'm talking about selling copies. We'll need some prints of one or two of his more notorious works. *Lovers*, for instance. That ought to fetch them in. Hope you got a quote on how he feels about the female sex from a personal angle."

"I'd have thought that was obvious considering the number of women his name has been linked with."

"Doesn't mean a thing. Could be a masochist."

"You're just a cynic," said Dale bluntly, and drew a sour smile.

"A little more hardheaded realism might stand you in good stead. How does that fiancé of yours feel about you spending a couple of days alone with another man? Assuming you were alone."

"Yes, we were." Dale eyed him steadily. "And Roger doesn't know I was out of town."

"And what he doesn't know he won't grieve about, eh?" with a shake of the grizzled head.

"Nothing happened *for* him to grieve about."

"But you're not taking any chances on having him

believe it. Can't say I blame you. Men tend to judge
others by their own inclinations. Few would be able to
last that length of time in close proximity to an attractive female without making some kind of pass.'' His
eyes registered her faint increase in color with sardonic
humor. "Think he'll be back down here by Monday?''

Dale held herself in with an effort. "He gave that impression.''

"Then you'd better have the copy ready for then. Be
another day out for you.''

She made her escape before she said something she
might regret, too well aware that he had been baiting her
deliberately. He could think what he liked about her relationship with Jos Blakeman. Certainly if he knew the
truth he would think the worst.

The office she shared with two other colleagues was at
the moment empty. Her desk was not, however. She
wrinkled her nose at the amount of work piled on it. Being away on a job for a few days was all very well, but
the catching up still waited one. She would have to set to
and clear up the backlog before she started on the
Blakeman write-up.

The designs editor popped his head around the door
sometime later, glasses catching the light from the window. "Ben tells me you've managed to corner that
sculptor chap," he commented. "Good going! What
will it run to?''

"About nine hundred," returned Dale, fingers still
poised above the typewriter keys.

The eyes behind the glasses blinked rapidly. "Cut it to
seven, if you can. It's got to fit around the artwork.''

"He means cut it to seven, period," remarked the
man seated at right angles to Dale, lifting his head from
some weighty tomb he was studying as the door closed

again. His expression was curious. "Did he mean Blakeman?"

Dale gave an inward sigh. "Yes," she admitted.

"So that's what you've been up to these last few days. He lives around London, doesn't he? What did you do—camp out on his doorstep?"

"More or less." Not for anything was she going to tell anyone else the full story. She had taken enough from Ben.

"So what's he like?" insisted the other. "Nobody ever got near him before."

"You'll find out when you read the interview," she returned edgily. "I don't have time to go into it now."

"Have a heart." The tone was quite unabashed. "Since when did I read the stuff we put out!"

Dale relaxed suddenly, leaning back in her seat to smile an apology across the two desks. She liked Nigel Martin, and usually got along well with him. "Sorry," she said. "I'm feeling a bit liverish this morning."

"Row with the boyfriend?" he suggested. "Or has our Benjamin been getting at you for taking so long out?"

She shook her head. "No, to both. It was Ben's idea in the first place. He said get it, so I got it."

"Wonder Woman rides again!" He grinned cheerfully. "I'd ask you to try teaching me your technique if I could apply it to the same advantage. Those eyes of yours would melt the stoniest heart! If we had true equality you'd be made to wear dark glasses."

"You just don't like acknowledging a superior approach," Dale came back on a mild note. "Now shut up and let me get this lot out of the way. I've an article to write."

She had a draft ready before four-thirty, and left a

copy on Ben Reynolds's desk for approval or otherwise. Any suggested changes would have to be made on Monday before she visited Jos Blakeman. She refused to think too much about that appointment as yet. She had a whole weekend to get through first, and other matters to consider.

Having brought a weekend case to work with her, Dale was able to travel via train and taxi straight out to the old, red-brick house outside Northwood that her great-grandfather had had built for a few hundred pounds around the turn of the century—as her father was in the habit of remarking during his frequent discourses on the present day cost of living. Personally, Dale had never really liked the house, finding the big, high-ceilinged rooms and bulky Victorian furnishings handed down with it overpowering. Victoriana might be an ever-growing cult, but for her it had to come in small doses to be even tolerable. She much preferred the pieces from other eras that her mother had introduced over the years in somewhat haphazard fashion—an intrusion her father tolerated only as a hedge against inflation, preferring the taste of his parents and grandparents to that of his wife.

Jennifer Ryland met her daughter in the paneled hallway, her still good-looking features lighting up.

"You're on your own," she said. "Roger not able to make it?"

"He's coming down in the morning." Dale had put down her case at the foot of the staircase. Now she put up a hand to smooth her windswept hair. "It's more like March out there than May! I hope it isn't going to stay so windy over the weekend."

"If it does we'll just have to make the best of it," remarked her mother with the air of one well accustomed to making the best of unsatisfactory situations. "Your father isn't home yet. Why don't we have a nice quiet drink together while we're waiting?"

"I wouldn't mind a cup of tea," Dale returned on a casual note, wondering if her mother was in the habit of taking a "quiet little drink" before her husband came home of an evening. "Traveling always makes me thirsty."

"It's a bit late for tea." There was a faint amusement underlying her tone. "But I expect Mrs. Tilson would make you some before she goes. I'll go and tell her."

"It doesn't matter," cut in Dale hastily, not wishing to delay the overdue departure of the lady in question any longer. "I can always make it myself. I thought Mrs. Tilson was supposed to leave at four."

"She is, but she stayed on to do some small extra jobs for me."

"What kind of jobs?"

"Oh, this and that," waving a vague hand. "She needs the extra money."

So work had been concocted in order to give it to her. Dale felt a warm affection flooding through her. "Forget the tea," she said impulsively. "Let's have that drink instead."

There was an empty glass already lodged on the octagonal table beside her mother's favorite chair in the drawing room. Dale affected not to notice it, asking for a dry sherry for herself.

"Very proper," came the equally dry comment as the glass was handed to her. "Six o'clock, sherry time!"

"It's closer to seven," Dale pointed out pedantically. "And I happen to like sherry."

"Well, I don't," swirling the gin and tonic in her own glass as she sat down. "I never did and I never shall."

"Mom." Dale's tone was hesitant. "What's wrong?"

"Wrong?" The smile turned on her was overly bright. "What on earth should be wrong? I've a good husband, a good home, my committee work—what more could any woman want?" She shook her head, her mood changing suddenly. "Don't mind me. It's been one of those days."

"I know what you mean."

"No you don't." It was a flat statement of fact. "You've got it all in front of you." She paused there, eyeing her daughter across the few feet separating them, her own face an older replica of the one before her. "Are you and Roger really serious about each other?"

Dale met the other brown eyes levelly. "As a matter of fact, he wants to fix a date for the wedding this weekend."

"Do you?"

The hesitation was scarcely noticeable. "It's time we got something settled I suppose. We've known each other more than a year."

"That wasn't what I asked."

Dale was well aware that wasn't what she had been asked. The trouble was she found it difficult to lie outright at the precise moment. Her father would be delighted, of course. He liked Roger. Her mother didn't—at least, not as a future son-in-law. Her next words confirmed that much.

"Dale, don't throw your life away. I don't care how eminently eligible Roger is. He won't make you happy."

"Why?" The hedging was deliberate—a play for time. "Why won't he make me happy?"

"Because he's dull. He lives by the book of rules."

"Like dad?"

There was no particular change of expression. "In many ways. And don't misunderstand. I love your father a great deal. He's a very fine man."

"But dull."

"That's right," on the same level note. "Dull. It isn't his fault, any more than it's Roger's. They see life one way, you and I see it another." She held up a staying hand as Dale attempted to speak. "Don't start denying it. I've seen your face when the two of them get talking together. I've watched you deliberately draw Roger's attention back to you because you can't bear being shut out that way. But you'll have to learn to bear it if you're going to marry him. He'll love you all right, but it will be in his own way and his own time." She paused there, head tilting. "Have you slept with him?"

Dale's eyes flickered her surprise. "I don't really think—"

"That it's any of my darn business?" Jennifer Ryland smiled a little. "I suppose you're right. I'd have resented it like anything if my mother had asked a question like that about your father. Not that she'd have even thought about it. In her book nice girls didn't do that sort of thing before they were married."

"Did you?" The question was out before Dale could stop it, her face flushing at the quizzical expression in her mother's eyes. "I'm sorry," she tagged on swiftly. "That's none of *my* business, either."

"Except that I don't mind answering," came the steady response. "No, I didn't. If I had I might have had some notion that we weren't quite as suitably matched as everyone seemed to think. I'm fairly sure you haven't, either. And Roger, being a gentleman, wouldn't dream of trying to persuade you too hard the way you'd really like him to." The smile came again.

"Don't look so taken aback. I might be able to give you twenty-odd years but I haven't passed the age of yearning for a Rhett Butler to sweep me off my feet. The only sweeping your father ever did was when he carried me over the threshold of this house, and that was purely to the book."

Dale's voice was hesitant. "You wouldn't think of leaving him, would you?"

"Now?" Jennifer shook her head. "I don't have anyone, or anything, to leave him for. It's too late for me. I don't want you to lose out on life, too, that's all. Think about it long and hard, before you start setting dates." She got to her feet at the sound of tires on gravel, setting down the half-empty glass. "Here's your father now. Let's leave the subject till tomorrow when Roger is here."

Dale remained where she was as her mother went from the room, brows drawn together. It was all very well to talk about waiting to see what else life had to offer, but for how long? Roger wasn't going to wait around indefinitely while she sorted herself out. To him it would be cut and dried. She either wanted to marry him or she didn't. And if this was the weekend when she was going to have to choose, then in all fairness to Roger it had to be a final choice. No going back on the decision afterward.

# CHAPTER FIVE

JOHN RYLAND came into the room a moment or two later, dressed as always in one of the conservative, dark business suits for which he had with some reluctance exchanged his former uniform of morning suit and bowler hat only a matter of some two years ago in deference to the new chairman's rather more progressive wishes. Now fifty, he had spent the whole of his working life with the same company, and had held his present position of group finance controller for the past eight years.

He looked every inch the executive, from the fast-graying dark hair right down to the tips of his highly polished black shoes, his weight carefully controlled to within a few pounds of what it had been when he was in his twenties.

"Hello, darling," he said, receiving Dale's kiss on his cheek. "Glad you could make it down. Your mother tells me Roger won't be here until tomorrow."

"That's right, I'm afraid. He was out of town until yesterday, so he has some catching up to do." She tagged on quickly, "He'll definitely be here though."

"Oh, I don't doubt that," with a smile. "When Roger says he'll do a thing one can always rely on his word. It's one of the things I like about your fiancé."

"Is there anything you don't like about him?" queried Dale on a light note, and drew a surprised glance.

"Not that I can think of. He's an excellent man. You're a very fortunate young woman."

"Don't you think he's fortunate, too?"

"Well, of course. That goes without saying." His tone was indulgent. "You mustn't read more than was intended."

One other trait her father and Roger shared, acknowledged Dale resignedly, was a total inability to know when they were being teased. "I'll try not to," she said. "Where did mom go?"

"To check on dinner." His eyes were on the glass still sitting where his wife had left it, a faint frown drawing his brows together. "Have you been here long?"

"About half an hour." Dale had followed the direction of his gaze. Now she added without haste, "We thought we'd have a quiet little drink while we waited for you. Can I fix you one?"

"I do wish you wouldn't use Americanisms," he said on a testy note. "We pour or mix drinks over here."

"Sorry," Dale did her best to sound penitent. "What would you like?"

"I think I'll join you in a sherry. Dry for me, too, please."

He sat down in his own reserved chair on the window side of the big, mahogany-framed fireplace while Dale poured the sherry, a small sigh of satisfaction escaping his lips. "I should go up and change first, but I suppose there's plenty of time. We're eating later tonight because your mother wasn't sure what time you'd be able to get here."

"Why bother to change at all?" asked Dale, bringing across the glass. "One suit is as good as another."

"I can't sit all evening in the same clothing I've worked in all day," came the anticipated response.

"Well, at least put on something casual. I won't mind."

"Then you should. That's the trouble with you young people today," he continued severely. "You don't have any standards."

"Even Roger?" she murmured, tongue in cheek.

"No, Roger is a little different," he conceded as she had known he would. "At thirty he's mature enough to set his own standards. I'm glad you chose an older man with a settled job. A very good job, I might add. He's done well."

Fleetingly Dale found herself wondering what her father would have thought of Jos Blakeman's professional achievements. Very little in all probability, although from a purely financial point of view, Jos must be streets ahead of Roger. Her father could admire a fine painting or piece of sculpture along with the next man, but whether he would be capable of seeing beyond the Blakeman predeliction for the female form to the artistry itself remained open to doubt. Not that he was ever likely to have to do so. Apart from the coming Monday, she would not be seeing Jos Blakeman again.

ROGER ARRIVED before lunch on the Saturday. With the wind died down and the sun shining, they spent the afternoon playing tennis at the local club, returning to the house in time to change for family dinner.

As no mention had been made of wedding plans, Dale had left the subject alone during the afternoon. Typically, Roger waited until they were halfway through the meal to bring it up, expressing surprise when John Ryland confessed to knowing nothing about the supposed discussion.

"I thought you were going to talk it over last night,"

the former said to Dale on a faintly censorious note. "I've been waiting for the verdict all afternoon."

"I've decided to wait till you got here," she said, avoiding her mother's eyes. "After all, the date has to concern you, too."

"Well, I'd prefer mid-July, if that's suitable to you, Mrs. Ryland?" His smile held charm. "That should give us all time to make our arrangements. If we don't find a suitable house before then we'll go on using my apartment. It's more than adequate for two. No point in rushing into anything, is there?"

"No point at all," agreed his prospective father-in-law with approval. "A house is the biggest single purchase a young couple are likely to make in their lifetime. It needs a lot of consideration. You'll be looking for an older property, I take it? None of these modern boxes."

"Definitely not." Roger's glance moved over the dining room, lingering on the silver displayed in gleaming splendor on the sideboard before returning to the table with its equally gleaming complement. "I'd like a house such as this one. There's room to move around in it."

"I'd prefer a smaller house," Dale put in, and saw the two men exchange similar glances. "And a modern one," she added defiantly. "Something I could shoot through at the weekends and forget about while I'm at work."

"You'll hardly be keeping on your job after you're married," exclaimed her father in tones of disbelief. "Surely...." He stopped at the slight shake of Roger's head, subsiding into his chair with a shake of his own.

"I'd rather Dale didn't continue in her job, of course," the younger man said smoothly. "But the choice has to be up to her—at least until we start a family."

"We haven't actually set a date for the wedding yet," Jennifer Ryland came in dryly, speaking for the first time in several minutes. Her gaze was on her daughter, drawing the brown eyes upward. "How about the second Thursday?"

"Of course. Our own wedding anniversary." Her husband sounded heartily approving. "Twenty-four years. It's quite an achievement in this day and age, wouldn't you say, Roger?"

"Very much so." He smiled across at Dale. "Wait until we're celebrating our twenty-fourth, darling."

Her own smile was weak. Twenty-four years from now she would be middle-aged and settled into a pattern of life that at this moment held little attraction. Was it so foolish to crave for something more exciting than that prospect?

Yet how long did excitement last? If she gave up Roger in order to go looking for it, she would be forsaking reality in search of a dream that might well turn into a nightmare when she found it. With a man like Roger there would be no disappointment because she knew exactly what to expect. Wasn't that better than taking a chance on some new and unpredictable emotion?

She avoided being alone with her mother again that evening, not wishing to be asked any more soul-searching questions. Jennifer, however, appeared to accept the situation, discussing arrangements to be made in a businesslike manner quite devoid of any lingering doubts.

By bedtime it had been decided that Dale was to have six bridesmaids, two of whom were to come from Roger's side. The guest list was already well into the two hundreds, with more to come. Far too many for the house, even with the addition of a marquee in the garden, John Ryland stated. The reception would be held instead at the largest and most luxurious of the local hotels, with selected guests invited back to the Ryland home for dinner in the evening, by which time bride and groom would already have left on their honeymoon.

With regard to the latter, Roger kept his own smiling counsel. It was to be a surprise, he said. Dale was not to know where they were going until they arrived.

"How can you be sure I'll like the place you've chosen?" she asked later when they were saying goodnight at her bedroom door. "Supposing I hated it?"

He laughed softly, rubbing a knuckle down her cheek. "You'll like it, it's one of the places I've heard you say you'd like to visit someday."

To visit perhaps, Dale thought, but a honeymoon was surely different? In which case it shouldn't matter where it was, she reasoned. Roger was simply trying to give her pleasure, and that was surely a cause for gratitude not censure.

Looking up at him now in the dim-shaded light of the landing, she felt a swift rush of emotion. She did love him; she really did. He was fine and honest, and so very good looking. What more could any girl want in a man? And what was she offering him that was so special anyway? She should think herself darn lucky that a man like Roger Shafton loved her enough to want to marry her in the first place.

Her kiss was tremulous, her voice low and husky. "Roger, don't leave me tonight," she pleaded. "I want you to stay with me. I won't change my mind this time."

His look held regret. "Dale, you know better than that. This is your parents' home. How could I possibly betray the trust they place in me." He put his lips gently to her temple, holding her close. "I know how you feel, darling, but having come this far we may as well go the full distance. After all, it's barely another two months."

A lot could happen in two months, Dale found herself thinking, and felt a sensation almost like panic sweep momentarily through her. Silly, of course. There was nothing to be afraid of. She was going to marry Roger.

MONDAY MORNING found Ben Reynolds in a surprisingly benign mood. "It's okay," he said of the article, which coming from him was unmitigated praise. "You'd better take it right out and let him see it. Ask if he'll approve it right away, will you, and wait till he does. He's ex-directory, so you're going to have to take a chance on his having got back."

"What if he doesn't approve it?" asked Dale tentatively, and drew a sourer glance.

"Persuade him. I don't want you back here till he has."

The journey gave Dale ample time for reflection. Recalling the details of her previous encounter with the man she was on her way to see did little to steady her confidence. In just four days he had become a stranger again, and one in whose predictability she placed the minimum of trust. He was more than capable of turning around now and refusing all permission to go ahead with the article. At least, she believed he was. After all, she was hardly going to broadcast the price she had paid for the material.

Backing onto the river, the Blakeman residence turned out to be large and Georgian, the grounds beautifully tended. The elderly man who appeared at the big, iron gate refused to say whether Mr. Blakeman had returned home or not until he had telephoned through to the house with her request for entry. He looked slightly more friendly on his return, swinging open one side of the double gates to allow her access.

"Can't be too careful," he said, closing it and locking it again behind her. "Mr. Blakeman doesn't see many callers." His sideways glance was curious. "Journalist, aren't you, miss?"

Dale was startled. "Is it so obvious?"

"Well," consideringly, "you're not that typical, I suppose, but you don't look much like one of his lady friends, either. Real glamorous they are." As if only just realizing he was talking out of turn, he did a hasty reshuffle. "Now that's not for publication, you understand. I've got a good job here and I don't want to lose it."

In which case he should learn to keep his mouth closed, thought Dale dryly, but refrained from saying so out loud. It wasn't the kind of tidbit she had any use for anyway. Let others plumb that angle—if they ever got the chance.

Inside, the house was sumptuous, the staircase unfurling like a fan from a hallway tiled underfoot in black and white. The walls were stark white, with huge vases of flowers set in alcoves, and gleaming mahogony furniture. Double doors led off each side, closed at present but suggesting the kind of spaciousness belonging to this era behind them.

"You look surprised," remarked the familiar sardonic voice from somewhere above her head, and she looked up swiftly to find Jos Blakeman watching her from the rail at the head of the staircase. "What did you expect?"

"Something rather less luxurious," Dale admitted,

recovering her wits with an effort. "You didn't seem interested in surroundings."

"To the point of spending time on them myself, no I'm not. I asked for the character of the place to be retained, and it was. I can live with the result."

And afford the cost. That didn't need saying. Appearances spoke for themselves. Dale watched him descend the stairs toward her, remembering that lithe movement, the controlled fitness of the lean body. She had been in this man's arms not so very long ago; had slept through the night with him by her side. It didn't seem possible.

The eyes that appraised her own shape in the trim, beige suit held an expression she found more than disquieting.

"I told you not to wear beige," he said. "Did you put that on purposely to tell *me* something?"

"I didn't even remember," she lied. "And I'm not in any position to throw out a perfectly good suit just because somebody happens to dislike the color."

"Not just somebody," he came back, unmoved. "Me. If you'd rather look less than your best...."

"Do you ever wear anything but jeans?" she flung back, and then stopped, aware how ridiculous the conversation was becoming. Catching his faint smile, she felt the telltale warmth rise in her face. "I brought the copy along for you to approve," she tagged on hastily. "My editor would like an immediate decision if possible."

"Would he?" The dark brows were lifted. "Then we'd better give it to him, hadn't we? Come on through here."

The room into which he showed her was beautifully proportioned, decorated and furnished with taste and discretion. Long windows at the far end opened onto a stone terrace, with green lawns stretching down to the water beyond.

"I've had the lower end under water a few times," Jos commented, accurately gauging her thoughts. "Nothing serious. You might have guessed I like to be close to the stuff. Something to do with being an Aquarius maybe." He took the file from her. "Have a seat while I look this over."

Dale obeyed, choosing a wing chair near the terrace doors. The sunlight was bright, the day warm enough to make sitting out of doors a feasible proposition. She wished she dared suggest it. But then she was hardly going to be here long enough to make it worthwhile, was she?

Jos took his time reading her work. Unable to bring herself to glance in his direction, Dale had no idea of his reactions, and could only sit there on tenterhooks waiting for the verdict.

He made no comment at all until he had finished, closing the file and tossing it down onto a nearby occasional table. "I should have offered you coffee," he said. "How about a drink and then lunch instead?"

Dale gazed at him nonplussed. "What about the article?"

"We'll discuss it over lunch."

Her heart sank. "Does that mean you don't like it?"

"It means," he said levelly, "that we'll discuss it over lunch. I might have one or two suggestions to make, that's all. Nothing radical."

"Then you don't really object to anything."

"There's little to really object to." His tone was dry. "I hadn't realized how dull a character I was."

Dale flushed. "I'm sorry—" she began, breaking off at the hard shake of his head.

"No, you're not. You wrote it that way because you didn't want anybody to guess we might have got any closer than interviewer-interviewee at any time. As far as the average reader will be concerned, you spent at the most a couple of hours asking stock questions and receiving stock answers. That wasn't how it was, but we'll let it pass."

*On what condition*, she wondered fleetingly, and put the thought to the back of her mind. "My editor likes it anyhow," she said stiffly.

"Your editor likes the idea of being first in the field with a Blakeman interview. How's he going to tackle it? A few photographs of my more conventional pieces to spice things up? *Lovers*, for instance. He wouldn't miss that opportunity."

"You sculpted it," Dale pointed out, and saw the strong mouth curl.

"Not as an exercise in erotica, believe it or not. I simply took Rodin's *Kiss* a stage farther."

"Several stages farther, according to some opinions."

"Including yours?"

The blue eyes held her pinned. "I didn't say that," she murmured weakly.

"No," he agreed. "You couldn't. I doubt if you'd know." Expression unchanged, he added, "Stay there while I go and tell Mrs. Girling you'll be here for lunch. I haven't finished with you yet."

Was that a threat, Dale wondered with an inner turbulence as he left the room, or a promise? She wasn't even sure which she wanted it to be. She had conditioned herself over the weekend into believing she could handle this man, but she realized now how false that notion had been. He could run rings around her any time he chose and she didn't have a single answer worth recording.

She was standing at the windows looking out toward the river when he returned. Without moving, she said, "When did you get back?"

"Yesterday." His closeness made her heart jump; he didn't appear to have had time to cross the room. "I'll be here now until after the show in five weeks."

"Will you be ready for it?"

"So far as it goes. What I haven't completed I don't show. It's as simple as that. I've two commissions to start on right after."

Dale still couldn't bring herself to turn around, knowing if she did she would find herself practically in his arms again. "Do you intend selling all of the works you'll be showing this time?"

"If I get the right offer for the right pieces.... Do you want that drink or shall we walk down to the water instead?"

"I'd like to walk, please."

"Fine." An arm came past her to depress the door handle. "After you."

Stepping out gratefully into the spring air, she said on a genuine note, "You really do have a lovely home."

"Not a bit Bohemian," he mocked her. "But then neither am I. I like beauty in any shape or form, not just when it comes female and unclothed." The pause was timed. "How's Roger?"

Dale had stiffened. "What you're really asking," she said, "is did I tell him about posing for you?"

"So did you?"

"No." She saw no reason to lie. "He wouldn't have understood."

"What wouldn't he have understood?"

"Artistic detachment."

"I'm not sure I understand it myself." He sounded amused. "I told you I could control my wilder impulses not that I didn't feel any. According to what you're implying, no artist ever wants to make love to a model because she's simply an object to him. Not true. There wasn't a single moment while I was sketching you that I saw you as anything but a very desirable, flesh and blood woman."

Color high, she said. "Why tell me now?"

"Because you need your illusions shattered from time to time. Of course, I realize it lessens the chances of you being willing to sit for me again."

They had reached the riverbank, which dropped considerably at this point. Dale gazed blindly down at the landing dock nestling below and the green-and-white gleam of the small but fast-looking craft moored there. A family of mallards splashed busily in the waterweed a few yards upstream.

"It removes it altogether," she said. "If I'd ever considered doing it again in the first place."

Jos bent and picked up a small pebble, lofting it into midriver where the water ran fast. "Supposing your fiancé found out about the first time?" he said on a seemingly casual note, and drew her eyes swiftly to his face.

"Are you threatening to tell him?"

There was no decipherable expression on the lean features. "I might if I thought it might get me what I want."

She didn't want to ask the question but the words were dragged from her.

"What do you want?"

"You." He said it without change of inflection. "You came here knowing that. I hope you're ready for the consequences."

"I came here because I was ordered to," she retaliated, ignoring the last. "I'm ready to leave the minute you give the word."

"Providing it's yes." He smiled a little at the flicker of uncertainty in her eyes. "Don't worry, it will be. We made a deal. Regarding the rest...we'll wait and see, shall we?"

"I'm going to marry Roger," she came back desperately. "We set the date this weekend."

"When?"

"July tenth."

"Two months. A lot can happen in two months." His gaze went over her face, lingering on her mouth. "You have a very sensuous lower lip, did you know that? Right now it's quivering in anticipation. I don't think we should disappoint it."

Dale made no attempt to resist as he drew her toward him. She knew herself incapable. This was what she had wanted since the first moment she set eyes on him again. Roger, the wedding, the whole world receded to a dim distance when Jos kissed her. She was conscious only of immediate sensations: the hard leanness of his body, the scent of his skin, the possessive demand of mouth and hands. At that moment she belonged to him wholly, and he knew it. There was fire in the blue eyes when he lifted his head.

"Come back to the house," he said softly. "We have a lot of catching up to do."

"No." Dale was yearning but determined. "This is as far as it's going." She pushed herself away from him, barely knowing whether to be relieved or disappointed when he let her go. "I'm marrying Roger!"

Jos made no attempt to take hold of her again, lip curling as he looked at her. "Even knowing you'll be cheating him."

"I don't intend cheating him."

"You already have in coming here."

"I was sent here," she protested. "I had no choice."

"There's always a choice. Having made it you're not going back on it."

She gazed at him for a long, tense moment, taking in the set line of his jaw. "How are you going to stop me? He might not like my having posed for you but he'd forgive me."

"If you're sure of that try telling him and remove the fear of his finding out."

"Jos." There was a sudden tremor in her voice. "Don't be like this! I'll admit to being unable to stay away from you, if that's what you want, but there's a world of difference between what I feel about you and what I feel about Roger. Attraction burns itself out when there's nothing else to feed on."

"But it's warming while it lasts and that's better than never getting lighted." The triteness was deliberate, mocking her own choice of words. His shrug a moment later seemed to signify a sudden loss of interest. "Have it your own way. Come and have that drink."

She wanted to ask for further reassurance but she knew he would not be prepared to give it to her. Whether he carried out his threat or not depended entirely upon his degree of determination. Right now it appeared to have lapsed.

They walked back to the house in a silence that was far from companionable. Ushered indoors ahead of

Jos, Dale stopped abruptly at the sight of the woman lounging in one of the chairs facing the windows. She was dark haired and strikingly good looking, her long-legged body clad in tailored slacks and a matching beige, silk shirt. Tawny-colored eyes held a certain speculation as they traveled from Dale to the man behind her.

"Hi," she said casually. "Hope I'm not interrupting anything. George said you were being interviewed but not by whom."

"George got it wrong," Jos replied just as casually. "The interview was last week, today I'm checking copy. Dale Ryland, *World Magazine*—Rowena Stewart, interior designer."

"Are you the one responsible for this place?" asked Dale, grasping the initiative before the other could speak. "From what I've seen of it so far, it's beautifully done."

"Thanks." The tone was pleasant but not particularly gratified, suggesting complete confidence in her own talents. "I thought you were still in retreat last week, Jos?"

"I was." He made no attempt to add to the statement. "What would you two ladies like to drink?"

"The usual for me, darling." There was a glint of challenge in the swift winging glance in Dale's direction. "I came begging for lunch actually, but if it's going to be inconvenient...."

"I imagine there'll be enough for three. There usually is." Jos was looking at Dale, his brows lifted with more than a hint of mockery. "Made up your mind yet?"

"Gin and tonic please," she said, refusing to let any possible innuendo affect her. "A weak one."

"A journalist who doesn't like alcohol?" Rowena

sounded gently derisive. "I thought it was the lifeblood of the whole profession! At least you work for one of the better rags." The pause was brief. "Tell me how you managed to persuade the man to grant you something he never granted anyone else—or is that a tactical secret?"

"There's a first time for everything," Jos put in before Dale could answer. He put a glass into her hand, eyes drawing hers upward despite herself. "With a show coming up I can use a little free publicity."

"You don't need any help in drawing an audience," stated Rowena, accepting her own glass from him with a smile straight into his eyes. "The trouble is usually in keeping them out."

"I'm not talking about an audience, I'm talking about keeping in the public eye."

She laughed. "I'm sure at least a couple of your new exhibits will do that for you—unless you've radically changed your style."

His shrug was light. "Perhaps I should. Surprise everybody."

"And disappoint not a few."

"Only those with one viewpoint." His glance came back to where Dale was seated, taking on some new element in the process. "What would you advise?"

"I don't think it matters," she retorted crisply. "You'll do as you want regardless." She put down her glass with a surprisingly steady hand. "I don't think I'm going to have time to stay to lunch after all. I'm due back in the office in less than an hour."

"Not without your copy," came the calm rejoinder. "And we haven't agreed on those alterations yet. Rowena has to pass close by your offices. She can drop you off."

"I wasn't necessarily thinking of leaving right after lunch," murmured the other. "There are one or two points I need to go over with you."

"Not today," Jos told her without a flicker of regret. "I'm stretching a point taking this much time off. I'll contact you."

Rowena bit her lip, but surprisingly accepted the dismissal. Dale stayed silent, trying not to think too deeply about the possible relationship between these two. It was nothing to do with her anyway. She wouldn't allow it to be. All she wanted from Jos Blakeman was his go-ahead for the article.

She got it after a luncheon memorable more for its silences than its conversation.

Handing back the copy, Jos said briefly, "Leave it as it is. There's nothing important enough to bother about."

Not any more, Dale surmised, sensing his hidden meaning. She had had her chance and turned it down. There would not be another attempt.

Seated beside Rowena in the sleek, white Mercedes sports car, she was aware of the other's controlled animosity, and was not too surprised when the questions started coming. She answered them with a brevity that left too much unsaid for total satisfaction, eliciting a growing frustration on Rowena's part.

"Was that scene you were playing at the bottom of the garden when I arrived part of the price you're paying for this article?" she asked in the end. "Or was Jos simply running true to form?" She glanced sideways when Dale failed to reply, lips twisting. "You do realize there won't be any follow-up, of course. With Jos it's either now or never."

It was what Dale had already told herself, so there

was no reason for the sudden stab of pain. Except that
no reason was needed where the heart was involved, she
acknowledged a moment later. And involved it was.
There was no more denying it.

"That's all right," she said, forcing a level note. "I
have all I want or need from Jos Blakeman right here."

THE BLAKEMAN ARTICLE sold a lot of copies. At least,
that was the way Ben Reynolds looked at it, and Dale
was not about to argue the point. Despite her personal
satisfaction with the final presentation, she had to admit
that it was geared to general-public taste in a way her
own might not have been, while at the same time doing
the sculptor himself no particular harm. And that, as
Ben was so fond of pointing out, was what it was all
about.

Roger took a different view, lip curling a little as he
scanned the page that evening in Dale's apartment.

"The man's a sensualist," he stated flatly. "He deals
in erotica not art! This belongs under the counter not on
top of it!"

The *this* to which he was referring was a three-by-
four-inch print of Blakeman's *Lovers*, presented in full
color and superbly lighted. Dale had never seen the original, which at present was on indefinite loan to an
Italian museum, but she had studied the photograph on
more than one occasion these past few weeks. The figures were slightly larger than life-size, she knew, yet on
paper, with no means of comparison, they could have
been mere inches long. Perfect in detail, they showed a
man and a woman naked together on a draped couch,
bodies entwined in an embrace that relied entirely on the
disposition of the viewer for interpretation. For Dale
there was a breathtaking ecstasy in the reaching hands

of the woman enclosing her lover with a passion that transcended simple lust.

"I think it's beautiful," she said with a hint of defiance. "The way love should be."

"In private between two people who love each other, perhaps—not as a public peep show!" He gave her a suddenly thoughtful glance, taking in the spots of color under her cheekbones. "This Blakeman character seems to have made something of an impression on you. When did you actually do the interviewing?"

"Oh, last month sometime. I don't remember exactly." Dale made herself turn and smile at him, adding lightly, "He wasn't an easy man to interview. It's something of a scoop to have done it at all."

"I wish you hadn't," Roger admitted on a serious note. "I'd rather not have my fiancé's name attached to this kind of thing."

"You mean my writing is so bad?"

"You know what I mean." He sounded impatient. "What's got into you lately, Dale?"

"Sorry," she offered, and meant it. She sighed and shrugged. "I'm not responsible for the photographs. I wouldn't have used that particular work, either. Not because I agree with you about it, but because too many will see it your way rather than mine." She studied the handsome features opposite, added on impulse, "Do you really think we're going to be compatible, Roger?"

The question caught him unawares; she could see that from the expression that sprang into his eyes. It took him a moment to answer. "If you have serious doubts perhaps we should find out here and now."

"I'm not going to bed with you on a purely clinical basis," Dale said sharply. "And I didn't mean just in that capacity, either. We don't even think alike."

"That's nonsense." He got to his feet and came over to where she sat, pulling her up and into his arms to hold her possessively. "Of course we're compatible. We always have been. You're just suffering from prewedding nerves, that's all."

Dale wished she could be as sure of that. She felt trapped. Yet if she called off the wedding now where did that leave her?

Free to go to Jos, came the thought unbidden, and she felt the tremor of longing run through her. Yet she couldn't, could she? There had been no communication between them since the day she had visited him, nothing to suggest that his interest in her was capable of resurrection. He had his work, and he had women like Rowena. Why should he need her? Even if he did there was no permanency in it. She was better off with Roger.

# CHAPTER SIX

THE INVITATION came through the mail the following week. Just a formal card granting entry to the preview of new works by Joseph Blakeman for one Miss Dale Ryland and guest. Dale contemplated tearing it up but found herself unable to do so. She wanted to go, she acknowledged wryly in the end. More than that, she had to go. It was the last opportunity she would ever have to see Jos again, unless by accident.

She mentioned the invitation tentatively to Roger, more than half expecting him to refuse to accompany her considering his views on the subject. Surprisingly he proved not only willing but almost insistent. He wanted, he said, to see what else the man was capable of turning out.

Thinking about that statement afterward, Dale wondered if it was the whole truth. Had Roger sensed her own deeper involvement? On one hand she doubted it—he wasn't the sensitive type—and yet neither was he normally interested in the arts, except as an investment. Perhaps that was it. Regardless of his personal view, a Blakeman stood to gain considerably in value over the years and might conceivably come within his means to buy. Roger was nothing if not practical when it came to money.

The gallery off New Bond Street was already well populated when they arrived around eight. Hessian-covered screens sectioned off the body of the floor into alcoves, each of the latter containing one or more exhibits lighted from above and below to reveal the finer points of both sketches and sculptures to their best advantage.

One or two of the smaller pieces were set on turntables, enabling the viewer to see the different angles without moving from the spot. Roger's attention was captured at once by the same head Dale had first seen in the house on the fens.

"Now that's what I call craftsmanship," he exclaimed admiringly, stopping in front of it. "I wonder what the price will be?"

"Try the catalogue," Dale suggested. Her own attention had been caught by the small crowd gathered toward the far end of the gallery, the focus of their interest concealed behind bobbing heads. That could be Jos over there in the middle of those people. His presence would naturally attract a crowd. She looked for some sign of the dark head, but too many others kept getting in the way. If it was Jos, he was keeping his audience entranced in a way she would not have thought natural to him.

Disappointment flooded her as the press parted momentarily to give a glimpse of the figure at its center. A bronze, by the look of it, set upon a low dias within a circle of white rope. She should have known Jos Blakeman would never allow himself to be cornered in that way. For all she knew, he had already left the gallery—if he had been here at all. But he must have been surely. This was his work. He had to attend his own show.

Roger appeared to have temporarily suspended interest in the head he admired, moving on to view the next exhibit with a calculating look in his eyes. Dale surmised he would be trying to work out which price might give him the best overall return on his investment, if he made one. He should have let caution go to the winds and taken the head if he admired it so much, she reflected dryly, glancing back in time to see a tiny yellow sticker being applied to the supporting stand. This wasn't the first piece to bear the Sold sign, either. She could see several others from where she stood.

The crowd around the bronze had thinned a little, allowing glimpses of the figure within as they progressed from section to section of the gallery. It was only when they finally reached the spot and obtained the first clear view that full realization came to Dale, and by then it was too late.

The figure was female, nude like all Blakeman females, and around half life-size. She was sitting with legs curled in front of her, arms lifted to hold the hair from the nape of her neck in a gesture that threw every slender curve of her body into exquisite relief, the soft gleam of the metal adding its own subtle highlights under the skillfully trained spots. The face was raised, its detail so finely modeled it seemed alive. *Shades* read the title plate pinned to the dais, at once arousing a dozen questions in the mind.

"That has to be one of the finest pieces of work Blakeman ever turned out," said a male voice right behind Dale as she stood there transfixed. "Wonder who the model is?"

"Whoever she is, you can bet he's keeping her to himself," replied another man with a sly little chuckle. "Wouldn't you?"

Dale forced herself to look at Roger who was still gazing at the figure, seeing the compression slowly growing around his jawline with a sinking feeling in the pit of her stomach. He knew who the model was. She was standing right there beside him. She didn't dare look at anyone else, afraid that they too might recognize her, although it wasn't really likely. Roger was putting two and two together and reaching the obvious conclusion: she could almost hear him thinking it. When he took her arm and turned her brusquely away from the stand she went without protest, aware that there was no getting out of what was to come.

They drove back to her apartment without speaking, the grimness around his mouth telling its own story. Only when they were inside with the door closed did he finally release the accusation.

"That was you back there," he said flatly. "Wasn't it?"

Dale hesitated before replying, even now looking for a way out. "It was my face," she agreed at length. "I don't—"

"It was you." The statement brooked no argument. "Do you think I'm a fool?" His gaze went over her as she stood there, the hurt and disgust plainly written in his expression. "You posed for that man, didn't you? *Didn't* you?"

"Yes." She let out her breath in a sigh. "But it wasn't the way you think."

"How many ways are there?" he demanded bitterly. "You took off your clothes for a man you'd never even met before when...." He paused there, eyes narrowed. "Or had you?"

Dale shook her head. "The first time was when I went to interview him for the magazine."

"And that was when he suggested you pose?"

"Not right away. That came later."

"After he'd got you into a suitable frame of mind, I suppose."

The sneer hurt but she refused to give way to the pain. "I told you it wasn't like that," she said through stiff lips. "All he did was sketch me. I thought he just wanted...I didn't realize he'd make me recognizable. He had no right."

"I see. You didn't mind having your body put on display for every Tom, Dick and Harry to leer at so long as they couldn't put a face to it."

"I wasn't even sure he'd use the sketches at all," she protested weakly, knowing herself caught in the web with no way out of it, but still impelled to make the effort. "He said I had a beautiful body and—"

"You have." It was said with bitterness. "Just how beautiful I hadn't fully realized, never having been allowed that much of an overall view before. I'm surprised he didn't want you up there alongside it for comparison—the living image as opposed to the graven. No doubt you'd have agreed to that, too."

"Don't be ridiculous!" She was angry herself now— an anger born more from guilt than any self-righteousness. "I've told you how it happened."

"No you haven't," Roger came back grimly. "You haven't told me anything, except that you went to interview the man. I'd be very interested to learn how you got from there to posing in the nude!"

"You wouldn't understand." She was holding herself in check now, aware that he would understand still less if the whole truth of the matter came to light. "Jos Blakeman is an artist. He doesn't see nudity the way you see it. He can stay detached—look at the human body simply as an object."

"Rubbish!" The derision seared. "The man who formed that figure back there did more than just study it from a distance. He *knew* it—intimately. He had to!"

Dale was still for a long, long moment before moving slowly and almost wearily to pull the ring off her finger and hold it out to him. "If you believe that," she said without expression, "then there's no point in going any farther. Goodbye, Roger."

He stared at her nonplussed, making no attempt to take the ring from her. "What do you expect?" he asked at last. "You've been so different these last few weeks. Can you really blame me for putting it down to Blakeman?"

"No," she said, still without inflection, "I don't blame you. I blame myself for not doing this before. It wouldn't have mattered then. Only to me."

"Did he make love to you?" The question burst from him as if he were unable to contain it a moment longer. "Tell me, Dale! I'm entitled to the truth."

"You're entitled to nothing. Not anymore." She took his hand and put the ring into it, closing his unprotesting fingers on his palm. "I'm sorry, Roger. You had a shock and you had a right to be angry, but that's as far as it goes. Please go now."

Pride came to his rescue, stiffening his back and immobilizing the handsome features. "I'll go," he said. "I'll be glad to. You were right the other day. We don't think the same way."

Dale waited until the door had closed behind him and his footsteps faded away down the stairs before sinking slowly to a seat in the nearest chair. So that was that. All over. She could feel nothing as yet. Perhaps she would continue to feel nothing. She hadn't wanted to marry

Roger. She could admit that now. He deserved better than she could give him.

Telling her parents was going to be the hardest part—at least where her father was concerned. Her mother would be secretly glad even if she failed to say so. She had never wanted the marriage to take place at all.

Sitting there, Dale wondered what her mother's reaction to the Blakeman sculpture might be. It was difficult to be certain. Somehow she had the feeling that censure would not be part of it. Thinking about it brought heat to her own cheeks. The press had been there tonight. Tomorrow's editions would be sure to carry some photographs of the new Blakeman works, with *Shades* as a sure-fire centerpiece due to its very presentation. That meant recognition at the very least.

Or did it? Not only were newspaper photographs notoriously bad, but was she really so recognizable? Only those who knew of her connection with Jos Blakeman were likely to have any suspicion at all, and even then she only had to claim a superficial likeness. The only way it could be proved would be if Jos himself came out and gave the name of his model.

Dale wished she could be sure of his silence on that score. She had trusted him to retain her anonymity completely but he had shown little compunction there. Anger stirred in her afresh. He had no right to go this far. Not without her permission. He could have put any face he liked to that body without making any difference to the overall impression. Why use hers?

She knew why, of course. He had told her why. To take her away from Roger. But it was weeks ago since he had used that threat. If he still wanted her why hadn't he made some attempt to see her between times?

The answer to that question was obvious, too. Retaliation, that was what it was all about. She had turned him down; this was his way of getting back at her. And he had succeeded all the way.

It was almost eleven before she could stir herself to begin getting ready for bed. She felt far from sleepy but there was nothing to stay up for. It was only after she had lain there for ten minutes or so that a warm drink began to seem like a good idea. It would help her to relax, perhaps put an end to the futile circling of her thoughts.

The kitchenette tiles felt cold beneath her bare feet. She heated milk quickly in the small saucepan and whisked cocoa powder into it before pouring it into a mug. Curled up on the two-seater settee on the other side of the partition, she sipped at the drink and tried to find solace in the thought of her freedom. But there was no solace. Just an overriding loneliness. She had lost Roger, now she had no one.

The soft buzz of her connecting outer doorbell brought a mingling of emotions. There was only one person that could be at this time of night. Roger had come back. She should have known, she reflected wearily, that he wouldn't be content to leave things the way they were. In all probability he had been sitting somewhere thinking the whole thing through, deciding eventually to give her another chance. But she didn't want another chance. Did she?

A second ring brought her reluctantly to her feet to place the mug down on the coffee table. He was pressing the bell under her name on the door plate, true, but the sound of it could penetrate through to the next apartment and disturb the occupants should he keep it up. She had to go down and let him in even if it was the last thing she wanted to do right now. She owed him that much consideration.

His shadow was visible through the glass of the outer door as she went quietly down the stairs. Opening it with a plea for quietness ready on her lips, she felt her breath catch in her throat as Jos Blakeman stepped forward into the dimly lighted hallway.

"Sorry to call so late," he said, not sounding it. "I had to shake off a lot of people." The dark brows lifted at the frozen look on her face. "Not inconvenient, is it?"

"It's almost midnight." Her voice sounded hoarse. "You'd no right to come here, Jos. Now or any other time!"

"I'm not interested in rights. I'm here because I wanted to come. Are you going to take me to your apartment, or would you rather I took you?"

"How do you know I don't have company?" she stalled, playing for time to steady her emotions.

"You mean your fiancé?" He shook his head with slow emphasis, mouth curving ironically. "When he left me an hour or so ago he was in no mood to come back here."

"What did you tell him?" It came out low but fierce.

"The truth. He was entitled to that."

"Your version of it, or mine?"

"I'm not sure what your version would be." He took her arm when she continued to stand there, turning her in the direction of the staircase. "Let's find some privacy. Then we can talk."

He was shutting the door behind him as he spoke, pressing her ahead of him, fingers firm through the thin material of her housecoat. Dale went because there seemed little choice, short of creating a scene right there in the hall. She could scarcely believe what Jos had just told her. Roger must have gone straight back to the gallery after leaving here, to accuse Jos of...what? It just didn't sound like him at all. Roger hated scenes.

She waited until they were safely inside her own door before releasing his grasp. Unconsciously, Dale put her hand to the place where he had held her, feeling his warmth still under her skin. The single lamp she had left on shadowed the hard-boned features, reminding her of the night he had carried her to the studio back at the fen's house. Only then it had been moonlight casting the shadows.

"Why did Roger come to see you?" she asked, low toned but resolute.

"To ask me a question and make me an offer," he said. "I'm not sure which took priority."

Her brows drew together. "An offer?"

"He wanted to buy the bronze on the proviso that he could have it removed from the gallery immediately."

Dale remained still, eyes fixed on his face. "Did you accept?"

"It isn't for sale." The statement was without equivocation. "I doubt if he'd have been willing to pay the price I'd be asking even if it were."

"I don't understand," she said carefully. "If it isn't for sale why did you bother sculpting it in the first place?"

"To look at," he said. "And for others to look at and covet the same way I've coveted the original since I first saw her. Shafton's wasn't the only offer received tonight—and it won't be the last."

"Just another Blakeman nude!" she said with bitterness, and saw his head move in negative response.

"Only to those incapable of seeing with more than one facet of their mind. Read Raymond Dalby's view in the morning. He sees more deeply than most."

"The same way you do?"

The sneer failed to touch him. "Not always. We'll just have to wait and see what came through to him."

Dale gazed at him with mixed emotions, wanting to hate him yet too well aware of his power to stir her. "You didn't have to use my face," she got out at length. "You could have left me that."

"It had to be your face. It was the only one that fitted the body." He made a small gesture that could have been construed as regret, except that she knew better. "Does it matter? You'd have to be standing right alongside for any comparison to be drawn."

"Roger knew."

"He would, wouldn't he. He was closest to you." He paused there, studying her. "I gather that isn't true any longer."

"That's the result you aimed for, isn't it," she demanded. "You had that invitation sent knowing he'd naturally be the guest I'd bring along."

He didn't bother denying it. "He wasn't right for you anyway."

"That wasn't up to you to decide."

"Somebody had to. If you'd gone ahead and married him you'd have been separated within a year." His tone roughened a little. "Why not face up to it? You're secretly relieved to have the decision taken out of your hands. Shafton could never have satisfied you. Not in any sphere."

"But you could, of course!"

He smiled faintly. "Try me."

A pulse throbbed suddenly at the base of her throat. "Just like that?"

"Not here and now. I meant on a more permanent basis."

"There's nothing permanent about what you have in mind," she came back in swift rejection. "You'd stay interested just as long as it took you to exhaust my potential, then it would be on to the next challenge. You've got the bronze. Be satisfied with that!"

He had hold of her before she was fully aware of his movement, pulling her up to him with a strength she couldn't fight. His body was as hard and muscular as she remembered it, his lips demanding a response in a way that left her helpless to resist.

She felt his hands moving over her possessively; the sensitive sculptor's fingers seeking and finding nerve endings she hadn't known existed until this moment, taking control of her senses. The heat rising in her seemed to come from her toes, reaching out to take over her whole body. When he stopped she felt deprived.

"I'm going to have you, Dale," he said thickly against her hair. "I won't let any other man take what's mine!"

"I don't belong to you," she whispered, shaken by the fierceness in him. "I don't belong to anyone!"

"But you're going to." He held her a little way away from him so that he could see her face, his own set in lines of hard determination. "If it's marriage you want, then we'll get married."

She stared at him in blank confusion, unable to believe he was really saying what he appeared to be saying. Barely an hour ago she had sat in this room yearning for what had seemed then so unattainable, and now Jos himself was offering it to her. If she wanted it.

"We don't have any basis for marriage," she got out at last, and saw his lips twist.

"What do you consider lacking?"

"Love, for one thing." She used the word defensively.

"Is that all? It's an overrated emotion anyway." He watched her for a moment, the hardness in him dissolving. "Consider the advantages. You want security allied to sexual fulfillment. I can provide both. What do you have to lose?"

"There's more to it than that," she protested. "There has to be!"

"You were going to marry Roger for less," he said. "He didn't even stir you physically."

"That's not true!"

"No?"

Dale held his gaze for only a moment before capitulating. "Why me?" she asked huskily. "You've known a lot of woman, Jos. Why do you want me so badly?"

"Because you're unique," he said. "Because your body has the most perfect structural balance I ever saw, and I want the copyright on it."

"To exploit?"

His hands tightened, hurting her. "*Shades* satisfied that part of me. If you'd done your homework more thoroughly you'd know I never sculpt the same subject twice. I can have a license through by Monday. That gives you the weekend to straighten things out here. We'll honeymoon in Paris." There was satire in the statement. "Did you ever see Paris?"

She shook her head, taking a grip on rationality. "It's ridiculous! Even if I did want to marry you, I wouldn't do it just like that. I'm not some *thing* you can take over anytime you want to. It takes two!"

"And you don't want the same things?" His smile held irony. "Prove that to me."

There was no evading his mouth, and after a moment

or two no real desire left to evade it. Everything else became of little importance when he kissed her like this, held her like this, his hands so sure of their way. Helplessly she found herself responding, body arching to the pressure of his fingers on her spine, moving to his guidance until the blood started singing in her ears. She was beyond thinking sensibly anymore. All she knew was that she wanted to be with this man making love to her now. He fulfilled a need in her that was more than just physical.

"I need time," she whispered against his skin. "Give me time, Jos."

"You have the weekend." His tone left no room for equivocation. "I'm prepared to wait till we've legalized matters."

"That wasn't what I meant." She looked up into the unyielding blue eyes, trying to ignore the message her body was still transmitting. "I was engaged to marry Roger until a couple of hours ago. As far as my parents are concerned, I still am. I can't break it to them over a weekend."

"Then don't," he came back, unmoved. "Present them with a fait accompli."

"I can't do that. They deserve to know first."

"So tell them you changed your mind. You're entitled to do that. They might not like it but they'll have to accept it."

That was as much as other people's feelings meant to him, Dale acknowledged numbly. She wished she had the strength of mind to tell him to get out, but knew it was beyond her. He knew it, too. It was there in the way he was looking at her.

"Do you want me to come with you?" he asked.

She shook her head swiftly, visualizing her father's reaction if she turned up with another man in place of his beloved Roger. "I have to do it myself."

His shrug left the problem entirely with her. "When do you plan on going down?"

"Tomorrow night—no, tonight, now. I always go down on a Friday straight from the office when I do go. They're expecting me this weekend."

"Roger, too?"

"Yes, he was going." She closed her eyes for a brief moment, opening them on a final desperate appeal. "Jos...."

"I'll be here Sunday evening," he said. "Be back." One hand came up to push back the hair from her face, falling again abruptly as if the action had been involuntary. His face was shuttered. "I'll come and fetch you if I have to, Dale. You're not changing your mind about this."

She believed him. What Jos Blakeman wanted he went right out and got, regardless of what stood in his way. "I'll be back," she promised.

"Good." He kissed her again hard, then put her from him. "I'd better go while I still can. It will give us both something to think about over the weekend."

She wanted to call him back but the words wouldn't come. Standing there in the subdued lighting after the door had closed on him, she tried to imagine what marriage to Jos was going to be like, failing completely because she still couldn't convince herself that it was really going to happen. There was so much she didn't know about him. How could she marry a man who was virtually a stranger?

THE MORNING REVIEWS of the Blakeman exhibition were, as always, mainly favorable, with *Shades* the main topic of discussion. As Dale had hoped, prints of the latter proved indistinct enough to make any kind of recognition doubtful, if not impossible, although the sheer artistry of the piece still managed to come across. It was going to draw a lot of people to the gallery to see it in the flesh, so to speak, and that worried her more. Luckily no one in the office seemed particularly interested in sculpture as an art.

Raymond Dalby wrote for one of the more serious dailies. Turning to the page, Dale ran a tentative eye down the column, not sure what it was she expected to find. There was no photograph and only a couple of paragraphs, but what he did have to say was pertinent in a way none of the other comments had been:

In Blakeman's latest study of "eternal woman" we have perfection as seen through the eyes of a perfectionist. A thousand ordinary mortals might try to analyze the particular pleasure they will feel in studying this bronze nude of a young woman at first glance little different from any other, and only one in that thousand comes close to the truth.

The secret lies in the very symmetry of this superbly executed figure, the proportions of both head and body in perfect balance. Can she exist, one wonders, or is she simply a sum of parts brought together by a mind grown weary of searching for an ideal? Whatever the answer, *Shades* is not up for sale at any price.

Dale put down the paper feeling more than a little strange. When she had thought about it at all, she had always accepted that she had a reasonably good figure, but it was not of the type that drew comment or elicited lascivious stares from passing males. Yet that wasn't what this was about, was it? Symmetry was the word

Raymond Dalby had used, not sensuality. It took an aesthete to find that aspect more worthy of a second glance.

What Jos felt for her was in the nature of an obsession, she acknowledged numbly. Having found what he considered the ideal, he wanted to own it. Not her, Dale Ryland, the person inside, but just a shell. In some ways it was worse than being wanted just from the sexual angle.

There were no comments from anyone at the office regarding the Blakeman exhibition. Nevertheless it was a relief to leave at the end of the day. Concern over how she was going to break the news to her parents grew in her on the journey out to Northwood. They would be expecting Roger to join them either tonight or in the morning, so there could be no delay in the telling—of that part of it, at least. It was the thought of trying to make them understand about Jos that worried her more. How could she possibly convince them that she knew what she was doing when she couldn't even convince herself?

Finding the right moment to start explaining any of it did not come easy. In the end it was Jennifer Ryland herself who precipitated matters with a casual mention of the Blakeman reviews over coffee.

"I'd have thought under the circumstances you might have been sent an invitation to the preview," she said. "After all, you'd met the man, and he obviously liked your write-up on him."

"I did receive an invite," Dale admitted with some reluctance. "I was there for a short time."

"More than long enough, I'd imagine," commented her father disapprovingly. "He doesn't appear to have changed his style very much. Does he ever sculpt anything else but nudes?"

"Yes, he does." Despite everything, something in Dale leaped to his defense. "It's just that he's particularly brilliant in modeling the human body."

"Especially when it's young and female." John Ryland shook his head. "Not that those who model for him are any better than he is!"

There was no stopping the run of heat under her skin. Dale could feel it in her face and only hoped it wasn't noticeable in the subdued lighting of the sitting room. She sensed her mother watching her from the chair opposite and tried to appear nonchalant. Not that there was any real danger of having that particular secret guessed. No one in this family would believe her capable of doing what she had done.

"Did you take Roger with you to the preview?" asked Jennifer suddenly, mentioning his name for the first time that evening.

Dale kept her eyes down. "Yes," she said.

"I shouldn't have thought it at all his kind of affair," John Ryland sounded surprised.

"Was it?" Jennifer insisted when her daughter showed no sign of answering. "Did he like what he saw?"

This time Dale had to look up, meeting the other brown eyes in fatalistic acceptance. "No, not at all." Her glance went to her father as she set down her cup. "There's something you're both going to have to know sooner or later, and it might as well be now. Roger and I have decided we don't want to get married after all. I'm sorry for all the trouble you've already gone to but... well, that's it. It's all off."

Her father was looking at her as if he had never seen her properly before in his life, his face a study in total bewilderment.

"You can't be serious," he said at last.

"I'm afraid so." Dale was fighting to remain matter-of-fact about it.

"We're just not suited, that's all."

"Suited?" He repeated the word in tones of disbelief. "My dear girl, you couldn't *be* more suited! Roger is exactly right for you."

"No, he isn't," she came back with dogged determination. "And neither am I right for him. We both know that now."

"When did you decide?" asked her mother with an odd underlying note in her voice.

"Last night." There was little point, Dale realized, in trying to prevaricate where her mother was concerned. She might not have realized the extent of Jos Blakeman's involvement in the matter, but she was almost certainly aware of some involvement; it was there in her eyes. "After we got back from the show."

"You mean you had a difference of opinion about Blakeman's works?" Her father sounded both relieved and exasperated at one and the same time. "Well, I can quite understand how Roger must have felt being dragged along to that kind of function, and if he spoke his mind you only have yourself to blame."

"There's more to it than that." That she could have convinced him of the truth in that statement in one moment had she cared to tell him the whole truth, Dale was fully aware, but she was not about to do that. "It's fundamental. We just don't see life the same way."

"Nonsense!" The exasperation was stronger now, the graying brows drawn together. "You don't know what you're talking about. You couldn't find a better man than Roger!"

"I know. It isn't a better man I want. It's..." Dale

stopped, raising her shoulders in a helpless little gesture.
"It just isn't Roger."

"Jennifer, speak to her." John Ryland appealed.
"Make her see sense!" He paused there, struck by
something in his wife's expression, his own undergoing
a sudden change. "Did you already know about this?"

"I guessed something might be wrong when I saw her
ring was missing," she returned quite calmly. "And I
don't think it's just a lover's tiff, either, I'm afraid."

"You never wanted Roger Shafton in the family, did
you?" came the sudden angry demand. "You've never
really liked him!"

"Not as much as you, no." There was a spark in her
own eyes now. "If you want the truth, I've always considered him pompous and old-fashioned!" Like someone else I know. The words remained unspoken but they
were there in the air, and it was apparent from the look
on his face that the implication had struck home. Looking from one to the other of her parents, Dale made a
small sound of protest.

"Don't," she begged. "Please don't upset yourselves
because of me!"

There was a brief pause before her father came stiffly
to his feet, expression controlled. "I'm not about to get
upset, as you so succinctly put it," he said. "I'll speak
to you again when you've come to your senses."

Two identical pairs of eyes met as he left the room.
Dale was the first to speak.

"You've hurt him."

"I know. It wasn't intentional." Her mother gave a
sudden rueful little smile, and shook her head in repudiation of that statement. "Yes it was. It always is.
There's a whole lot of truth in the words of that song.
We'll get over it. I'll go along in a little while and

smooth things over." She studied her daughter for a long moment, expression difficult to define. "In the meantime supposing you tell me the real reason you and Roger broke things off."

Dale's gaze slid away. "I already told you."

"No, you didn't. That was the only version you could give your father." The pause was significant. "Does it have something to do with Jos Blakeman?"

The golden head came around with a jerk. "Roger didn't have any cause to be jealous of Jos."

"Didn't he?" The question was soft.

"No!" Faced with the steady regard, Dale felt the anger fade from her. "Not in the way you mean," she tagged on wearily, and saw the smile come again.

"How many ways are there? If I'm right in what I'm thinking, he had every cause. He recognized that sculpture, didn't he? He knew you'd posed for it. I thought there was a passing likeness myself when I saw the newspaper this morning, but I told myself that was all it was."

There was no use in denying it. Dale gave a defensive shrug. "I only sat for a few sketches in return for that interview. I wasn't to know what he had in mind."

"According to what you said in the article, he rarely uses a live model for the actual sculpting," her mother reminded her dryly. "And he didn't come across as the kind who'd bother with a subject he didn't intend using. What you really mean is you trusted him not to make you recognizable."

There was resignation in the reply. "All right, so I trusted him. Gullible of me perhaps, but there it is." She studied her mother curiously. "You're not even a little bit shocked, are you?"

"From what I've seen of it there's nothing about the

figure to shock anyone. It's beautiful. You should be proud not ashamed.''

"I'm not ashamed," Dale protested, then hesitated. "Not really."

"Embarrassed then?" the other suggested. "You don't like to think of people who know you seeing you that way. I don't think you need worry too much. The only person who knows your identity is Jos Blakeman himself, and there's no reason for him to divulge it." She paused, tone changing. "What's he like? Really like, I mean. You barely touched him in that interview."

Dale's eyes flickered. "What makes you think I got any closer?"

"Your attitude whenever his name is mentioned. Nobody tightens up like that over someone who means nothing to them."

"I'd rather not talk about him anymore." She got jerkily to her feet. "I'm tired. I think I'll have an early night."

"Bottling it up won't help." Her mother's expression held sympathy and understanding. "You're having an affair with him, aren't you, Dale? That's what really broke you and Roger up."

"No. No, I'm not. It isn't like that." Dale sat down again suddenly, knowing she had to talk about it—glad of someone she could talk to. "He could have had an affair," she admitted wryly. "I don't think I could have held out if he'd really put his mind to it." She paused, still hardly able to credit that last night wasn't all a dream—or a nightmare. "That isn't what he wants." Meeting her mother's eyes, she gave an awkward little laugh. "He wants me to marry him instead of Roger. He even made sure Roger saw the bronze."

There was a note of approaching envy in Jennifer's voice. "He obviously doesn't let minor details put him off. So where's the difficulty?"

"I'm not sure I love him. I know he doesn't love me."

"You mean he's told you so, or he just hasn't said the actual words?"

"He doesn't have to tell me so. He doesn't believe in love as an emotion. With him it's all physical. Well, not quite all." She floundered for a moment, uncertain how to explain her meaning. "I think he sees me something like a collector's piece. One he wants to own. He's willing to pay any price—including marriage."

"Perhaps he regards marriage as the only sure way to keep you." The other voice was soft. "Was what you felt for Roger love, do you think?"

"Yes," Dale rejoined slowly. "Of a kind."

"A very boring kind. You wouldn't have stood it a year."

"That's what Jos said."

"Did he? He seems to understand you, anyway." Jennifer hesitated, studying her daughter's uptilted face. "Dale, you're the only one who can really know how you feel," she said at last. "But ask yourself one question. Can you bear to turn him down?"

"He isn't giving me much opportunity." Her mouth felt dry. "He's arranging everything for Monday. If I don't go back he'll come down here to get me. That's what he said."

"And you believe him?"

"Yes, I believe him." She gave a tiny shiver. "He can be quite ruthless when it comes to what he wants. That's what scares me. There's no softness in him."

"There will be. It's up to you to find it."

·It was a moment or two before Dale could bring herself to ask, her eyes searching her mother's face, "Are you telling me to go ahead and marry him?"

Jennifer shook her head. "I can't tell you anything. I wouldn't even try. All I will say is it's sometimes better risking hell than settling for safety. Why don't you sleep on it? If you do decide against it, then obviously nobody is going to stand by while he takes you out of here. I doubt if he'd even attempt it."

Dale wasn't so sure. The way he'd said it last night, he was more than capable.

"I'll never sleep," she said. "I hardly slept last night. It keeps going around and around in my mind. Supposing I did marry him. What would happen if I lost what he seems to find so vital?"

"If what Raymond Dalby says is right, you don't stand to lose it. It's your skeletal structure they're all raving about, not your voluptuous curves."

Dale had to smile. "You make me sound like a bag of old bones!"

"That you're not, and you know it. 'Perfectly formed,' Dalby said. It makes *me* feel quite unique to have given birth to such a prodigy." Jennifer let her own smile die a natural death. "He might not be in love with you now the way you'd like him to be, but he could learn. All he needs is the incentive."

Dale's tone was low. "And what about me—the way I feel?"

"I think you already know the answer to that. All *you* need is a little courage."

Gazing at the older face so like her own, Dale said softly, "You'd take that chance, wouldn't you?"

"Like a shot," came the ready response. "But then I'm looking at it from the other end of a good safe marriage. Go and have that early night. Things might seem clearer in the morning.''

Dale had doubts about that, but she got up anyway, leaning down impulsively to kiss her mother's cheek. ''Thanks for listening. And for the advice. You've given me something to think about.''

## CHAPTER SEVEN

THINK ABOUT IT was all she did for a good part of the night, and without reaching any definite conclusion. When it all boiled down, her mother was right; courage was what she needed. She wanted to marry Jos, but she wanted it the conventional way, with everything in the garden rosy. Only Jos wasn't conventional, and never would be. If he came to love her at all it would be in his own way, and that might not be hers.

She dozed eventually, awakening at seven with the problem still weighing her down. The morning was long and fraught, with her father going out of his way to avoid having to speak to her. She knew the news of her breakup with Roger had hit him hard and deep, and tried to make allowances for his attitude. Yet she couldn't help feeling hurt by it. Roger might have been the kind of son he had always wanted, but her happiness should surely count with him, too. He couldn't expect her to marry a man simply to satisfy his own wishes.

"Leave him to get over it," advised her mother after a silent and uncomfortable lunch. "He's disappointed about things right now, but it will pass."

"I think I might go back to town," said Dale, unable to stand the thought of another day of this kind of atmosphere. "What about all the arrangements?"

"I'll deal with that." Jennifer spoke firmly. "And don't worry about things. Your father will see how useless it is to be like this once he's had time to think about it."

"Except that he doubts if I'm capable of knowing my own mind," Dale came back wryly. She met her mother's eyes and gave a brittle little laugh. "I'm not sure he's all that wrong."

"You still haven't decided?"

"No."

Jennifer deliberately lightened her tone. "From what you tell me, you'll have it made up for you come tomorrow night."

"If I'm still there." Dale shook her head. "Oh, don't worry, I'll make sure he knows I'm not down here still."

"I'm not worried," her mother denied. "In fact, I'd like to meet him." The smile came again. "On the other hand, I don't think your father is ready for any more shocks. Phone me tomorrow night and let me know which way it went, will you? I'll make sure to answer the phone."

It was past five by the time Dale reached the apartment. With Jos not expecting her back in town until the following evening there was no immediate need to think about what she was going to do. Her mind was numb with thinking anyway. Tonight she was going to relax. Forget about Jos—forget about everything.

A long warm bath went a long way toward relaxing her. She wasn't hungry, but she forced herself to eat a sandwich and drink a cup of coffee around six-thirty.

The knock on her door coming when she was halfway through her coffee caused her to choke on the contents, reminiscent as it was of the last time she had received a visitor. For a moment or two she contemplated ignoring the summons in the hope that whoever was outside would assume the apartment was empty, until the knock came again, louder this time, followed by a voice that brought her swiftly to her feet.

"Dale, I know you're there."

She opened the door with reluctance looking at the familiar handsome features without expression.

"I thought we said everything there was to be said the other night," she stated flatly.

"I called the house," Roger said, ignoring the lack of welcome. "Your father told me you'd come back to town."

Her smile lacked humor. "I suppose he told you how upset he was about our engagement being off, too?"

"Yes, he did. That's what I've come to talk to you about." He hesitated, glancing toward the stairs. "Can we go inside?"

Dale stood back resignedly, acknowledging his right to that much consideration. "How did you get in anyway?" she asked for want of anything better to say.

"The girl from the next floor up let me in with her." He closed the door and stood there for a moment looking at her, a variety of emotions mingled in his expression. "I went to see Blakeman on Thursday night after I left you," he said. "I offered to buy the bronze from him."

"Why?" Her tone was carefully controlled. "It had already been on view."

"But only he knows who the model is. I asked him that."

"And?"

His voice went flat. "He wouldn't sell—wouldn't even quote me a price. So I asked him something else." He paused there, eyes darkening. "You did sleep with him, didn't you, Dale?"

In her mind's eye she could almost see the curl of

Jos's lip as he answered, sense his amusement at the use of the euphemism. The opportunity had been handed to him on a platter; he hadn't even had to lie about it.

To try explaining seemed a waste of time and effort under the circumstances. She doubted if it would sound believable in any case. She said harshly, "Did you come back just to tell me you'd had your suspicions confirmed?"

He seemed to gather himself then, as if in preparation for a speech he had rehearsed.

"No," he said. "Not just that. I've had time to think things over this last couple of days, Dale. I can't pretend that what happened between you and Blakeman doesn't matter to me, but I realize the blame has to lie mostly with him. He told me how you were cut off by the floods and had to spend two nights at that house with him. That made it a little easier to understand. For a man of his experience, it would be a relatively simple matter to play on the danger, put you in need of reassurance. He even admitted that you only posed for him under pressure, too. Do as I say or I'll tell your fiancé what you've done! That was it, wasn't it?" He took her agreement as read, voice hardening. "The man's nothing short of a blackmailer!"

Dale felt dazed, unable to take in what he appeared to be trying to say. "Are you trying to tell me you're prepared to forgive and forget what happened?" she got out.

"I suppose that's the essence of it—although it might take me a little time to forget it completely." His smile was only slightly stilted. "We all make mistakes. We shouldn't be expected to pay for them the rest of our lives. Whatever you've done, I still want you, Dale."

It was a moment or two before she could bring herself to speak. In the end she said softly, "You know, you're almost too good to be true, Roger. There can't be many men who'd be willing to overlook something like this."

"You weren't emotionally involved with the man," he came back in the manner of one determined to be convinced. "It was simply a physical thing, wasn't it? The way it sometimes is when two people are thrown together in certain circumstances. I only wish you'd found it in yourself to tell me about it before, instead of leaving me to find out the way I did, but I suppose you hoped it would never have to come out at all if he failed to use you as a subject."

"Something like that." Dale had barely listened to the last few words, her mind on something else he had said. "Did it ever happen to you that way?" she asked softly.

He took her meaning at once, his face flushing a little. "Yes," he admitted. "It was before I met you, but I can remember enough about it to know how easily it can happen—especially in close confines."

She longed to ask for more detail but doubted if he would be prepared to go that far. It wasn't his mistakes they were here to discuss. The question now was how she would tell him what she had to tell him.

In the end there was only one way to say it and that was straight out.

"Roger, you're a very fine person, and I'll always be grateful to you for trying to understand, but I can't marry you. It wouldn't be fair to either of us."

Rejection was the last thing he had anticipated; she could see that from the expression that sprang to his eyes. He had come here with what must have seemed to him a munificent gesture, and she had thrown it in his face. Comprehension was slow in coming.

"I was wrong, wasn't I?" he said bleakly. "Blakeman does mean something to you. Have you seen him again?"

"Yes." She hadn't intended to say it, but she found herself doing it regardless. "He asked me to marry him."

"I see." There was bitterness in his voice. "I've made a fool of myself, haven't I? Why should you want me when you can have the great Joseph Blakeman!"

"I said he'd asked me, not that I'd accepted." Her own voice shook suddenly. "I don't want to marry anybody. It's too much like stepping into prison!"

"I see," he said again. This time the statement held finality. "I'll leave you to it then."

"Roger." She made a small gesture of appeal as he made a move toward the door. "I'm sorry."

He didn't turn. "So am I. Goodbye, Dale. I won't bother you again."

She began moving almost before the door had closed, her mind already made up. She had meant what she had said a moment ago. She wasn't going to marry Jos. Not, at least, until she had had time to really think things through.

If she were here when he came to find her tomorrow night there was no doubt he could persuade her. When he had hold of her she was incapable of saying no to anything, and he knew it. So she simply wouldn't be here. She would go away. Where, she didn't know, and didn't much care. Anywhere would do so long as it was far enough. She had a week's holiday owing, and there was nothing pressing for immediate attention at work. Ben Reynolds wasn't going to be pleased about her taking leave of absence without prior notice, but that was something she would have to face when she got back—along with Jos himself. At least it would give her breathing space.

SHE SPENT THE WEEK at a tiny hotel outside Oban, taking short walks amid the breathtaking scenery on the fine days and spending the not so fine curled up with a book in the small but cozy lounge. It was the tourist season and the hotel was full, but no one bothered her, too intent upon making the most of their own breaks from routine in daily excursions to the mountains, lochs and forests of the Western Highlands.

It took time and a lot of self-examination before she finally came to the decision that she wasn't going to marry Jos. He was no more right for her than Roger had been. What she needed was a compromise between the two—a man who could stir her physically yet show tenderness, too. There had to be one like that somewhere. Either she would find him or he would find her. It was worth waiting for, she told herself firmly. No matter how long it took.

The journey back to London was long and tedious, giving her too much time to dwell on forthcoming, unavoidable events. The memory of Ben Reynolds's reaction when she had telephoned him from Oban the previous Monday morning made her coming return to work something to regard with despondency. He had been at his most sarcastic, receiving her stumbling explanation with obvious skepticism. Young women her age did not in his book require sudden and urgent rest from the stresses and strains of everyday living, she had gathered from the brusque comments. Not without very good reason anyway, and that she was not supplying. She was going to have some pertinent questions to answer come the morning.

The knowledge that she was going to have to face Jos at sometime was something she didn't want to think about at all. When the time came she would be ready for it. She was determined to be ready for it. There was no way he was going to persuade her to change her mind. She had suffered too much in making it up.

Despite everything it was good to be back in familiar surroundings again. Putting her key in the outside lock, she wondered how long it would take Jos to discover she was home. A couple of days, if she were lucky. Unless he had taken the hint. She knew that was hardly likely. He wouldn't give up that easily. He would be here, sooner or later. She could only hope it would be later.

She was still struggling with the lock on her own apartment door, which was always stiff when not used for a while, when the hand came around from behind her to take the key from her and turn it with one swift flick of a lean brown wrist.

"Welcome home," said the all-too-familiar voice on a hard note.

Dale walked into the apartment ahead of him as he pushed open the door, determined to give any unseen listener little satisfaction. There was only one way Jos could have got into the house, and only one person likely to have let him in. Her upstairs neighbor was a mite too helpful at times.

Her heart was thudding like a trip-hammer. Whatever she had anticipated, it had not been this swift a confrontation. It was almost as if the week between had never existed.

"I didn't see your car outside," she said without looking at him.

"You weren't intended to. I parked it around the corner." He took the suitcase from her, slinging it to one side with a gesture that betrayed his mood more forcefully than any words. "What was this supposed to prove?"

"That I'm not available to order," she retorted with a

sharp lift of her chin. This time she made herself meet the blue eyes, quelling a desire to run from the purpose in them. "Jos, there's nothing you can say or do that's going to make me change my mind now. Tomorrow I'm going back to my job and—"

"You don't have a job," he said, jerking her up short. "I've taken care of all that. I've given in notice for the apartment, too."

Dale stared at him in shock, her mind refusing to take in the full import of what he was saying.

"You can't have," she got out at last. "No one would take your word for it, just like that!"

His smile was tilted. "It depends on circumstances. Your editor jumped to an immediate conclusion when I told him you didn't feel up to coming back to work, and said you weren't to worry about anything. I think he feels partially responsible for having initiated our meeting in the first place. As for this place...." He paused and shrugged. "The owners were only too eager to accept. They can charge a higher rent to a new tenant. I told them it would be vacant after the weekend. All you'll need are your personal things. The rest can stay." He registered the protest forming on her lips with a challenging glint. "I'm not taking anymore chances on you running out on me. I'm taking you back with me tonight. By this time tomorrow we'll be married and in Paris."

"No!" She had meant to say the word firmly and clearly, but it came out as little more than a whisper. "Jos, you can't take over my whole life this way. I won't let you!"

"You can't stop me," he said. "And if you've any doubts about that, there's one way to disprove them."

She fought him as he swung her up in his arms, but made no impression. Pinioned against his chest, she felt him move toward her bedroom with a mingling of emotions in which fear played only a minor part.

Only when he put her on the bed in the soft golden glow of evening sunlight did she finally surrender herself to the knowledge that this was what she wanted, too—what she had wanted from the first. No gentle persuasion but sheer overwhelming assertion, opening the floodgates on the innermost recesses of her mind.

THE ONE PREVIOUS TIME Dale had visited Paris she had been with a school party, and she remembered little of it except that it had rained almost constantly the whole week. With Jos it was another city, the Paris of her imagination, full of color and life. He knew it like a native and treated it like a second home, greeted in some places by name and in others like a brother.

Seen through his eyes, the treasures of the Louvre took on new meaning. Both there and in the other galleries, they would sometimes turn from a work he had been explaining to her to find a small group gathered to listen in evident appreciation. Recognized on a couple of occasions, he simply took Dale's arm and made a firm if unhurried getaway, refusing to alter the habit of years when it came to personal privacy. His life, he said, was his own. He owed no one the right to intrusion.

At the Musée Rodin he forced her to look beyond the apparent eroticism of many of the pieces to the mind of the man who had executed them, to make her understand, if even only in part, the admiration amounting almost to worship of the human body that lifted his expression of physical love above the obscene. Try as she might, Dale couldn't always find it in herself to agree with him. To her, the chaste adoration of the *Eternal*

*Idol* far outweighed the sheer carnality of such works as *L'Emprise*.

The fact that Jos could rouse her to a sensuality approaching and sometimes equaling that expressed by the sculptor was something she tried not to think about too deeply, but only when she was actually in his arms was it possible to forget the lack of purifying emotion between them. Getting close to the man she had married in any sense but the physical was not going to be easy because he refused to allow her access to his inner self. By the time they were due to return to England, she had learned a great deal about art, a little less about herself and nothing at all about Jos Blakeman outside of what he wanted her to know.

She had written to her parents from Paris, stating simply that she was married to Jos and asking her father to forgive her for any unhappiness she had caused him. Her mother's communication to the effect that he was not yet prepared to do so came as no great surprise, yet it still hurt. She had thought of her father as a man of balanced judgement, if little humor, and had loved him that way. His attitude now defied any kind of balance. It was that she found so hard to accept.

Beautiful as she found the house on the river, after three weeks there she still felt like a temporary visitor. With Jos busy working on the two commissions he had told her about, and the services of a small but more than adequate staff, she found little to occupy her time.

Her suggestion that she should find herself another job was met with a blank refusal. If she was bored, Jos said sardonically, she should find herself a hobby. If she wanted to try painting he could supply the materials.

Accepting the offer in a fit of pique Dale found herself almost immediately regretting it. She had been rea-

sonably good at art at school but had not so much as
lifted a brush since. Yet with the first tentative stroke of
azure blue across virgin white she felt something in her
spring to life. Creation, that was what it was about, the
very act of forming something with one's own hands; of
seeing shapes appear where before there had been only
blankness. If she never produced anything worthy of a
second glance, at that moment it hardly seemed to matter. She had found something she wanted to do.

Her mother's request to come and visit her came
toward the end of August. Her father was away from
home for a week, she said, leaving her free to take advantage of the opportunity without him having to know.

"Ask her to stay a couple of days," said Jos without
too much interest when she put it to him over dinner that
evening. "It will give you something to think about."

"I have things to think about," Dale returned coolly,
resenting his indifference, and he lifted his head to look
at her, brows lifting in the mocking manner she had
come to detest.

"Oh, yes, your painting. When am I going to see a
sample?"

"Never, if I can help it."

"Scared of a little criticism?"

"From you it wouldn't be a little and it wouldn't
make allowances. Yes, I'm scared. I enjoy my dabbling.
I don't want to be put off."

"All right, so dabble away." He was smiling but with
a hint of impatience now. "You don't have much
courage, do you, Dale?"

"I had enough to take you on," she said, refusing to
be drawn into what he wanted her to say.

"You had a choice?" There was irony in his voice.
"Odd, I don't remember it quite that way."

Dale didn't, either. She remembered it the way it had been. Jos had allowed her no mercy that night, nor any night since. When he wanted to make love to her he did it, regardless of what she wanted. To be honest, she had to admit that so far he'd never failed to arouse her, but come a time when he couldn't, she doubted if it would make much difference to him. What he wanted he took.

"What's going to happen when you've had enough of me?" she inquired with a deliberation of her own. "Do I go on the reject pile?"

The glint in his eyes was a threat in itself. "I haven't decided," he said. "When the time comes I'll let you know."

"Until then just keep yourself available." Her tone was light but with an underlying edge. "That's what it amounts to, isn't it, Jos? The longest time we spend together is in bed!"

"I can think of worse places." The glint had become a gleam, the set of his mouth warning her to stop right there. "I can think of other places, too, if needs be. I wouldn't want you to get bored."

"I'm not bored," she said, relinquishing the unequal battle before he was moved to make her. "I just wish...." She broke off abruptly, shaking her head. "Forget it."

"Wish what?" he insisted. There was an odd note in his voice. "Tell me."

"It doesn't matter." Not for anything was she going to tell him what she had been going to say. It didn't matter a damn to him whether they got any closer or not. Why should it? He had all he had contracted for. "It's all right to tell my mother to come then?"

"Why not?" The indifference was back. "A girl needs her mother."

JENNIFER RYLAND arrived the following Tuesday. Greeting her, Dale thought she looked older—or was it just that she hadn't seen her for so long?

"I'm glad you came," she said. "I've wanted to come home but.…"

"But it's still not advisable," her mother confirmed. There was a wry quality in her eyes. "I'm afraid it's going to take a long time. He might have managed to accept Roger's loss eventually, but it really finished him when you wrote to say you'd married Jos Blakeman. It's only fortunate your name never came up in connection with the sculpture. I think he'd have died a thousand deaths rather than know about that." She paused, studying her daughter's face. "Who has it now?"

"It's here. In the studio." Dale refrained from adding that she never went up there herself so consequently hadn't seen it again since the night it had been on view at the gallery. Nor did she want to see it. "Jos says it gives him inspiration."

Her mother's glance held speculation. "Do you sit for him?"

"No. He never uses the same subject twice. Not in sculpting anyway." She regretted the last remark the moment she had made it, knowing her mother was far from dense. She had got into this marriage on her own; she would handle it on her own. No angling for sympathy. She changed the subject quickly. "Where did dad go?"

"On a week's business seminar, much to his disgust. He thinks the company is becoming far too Americanized. I don't see how he can expect much else considering they're the major stockholders but—" she gave the wry shrug again "—he doesn't adapt to change easily. There's talk of his having to make a trip to the States in the near future. Quite a lengthy one."

"Shall you go with him?"

"If I get the opportunity." Jennifer had walked across to the drawing-room windows and was looking out on the view over the river. "This really is a lovely place, Dale. I expected something a little more...." She paused, searching for a word that would adequately express her meaning.

"Garretlike?" suggested Dale brightly. She laughed. "Don't get the wrong idea. Jos can live just as well in either. He bought this place on the advice of his accountants as an investment. When he tires of it he can always sell it to some rich Arab and retire on the profit."

Her mother turned and gave her a swift searching glance but made no comment. "What do you do with your time while Jos is working?" she asked instead.

"Oh, this and that." Dale hesitated, not certain whether she wanted her mother to see her daubs, either. "I paint a little."

"If you can't beat 'em join 'em?" on a dry note. "What does Jos think of your talent?"

"He hasn't seen anything I've done." She refrained from saying she had no intention of letting him see. "I have what used to be the garden room here on the ground floor. I respect his domain and he respects mine." She came to a sudden decision, getting to her feet. "I'll show you what I've managed so far then we'll have tea. How long are you able to stay?"

"Until Thursday afternoon. Your father gets back Friday."

"Good, that gives us two clear days."

The garden room overlooked the side gardens stretching across to a tennis court half-concealed by box hedging.

"Does Jos play?" asked Jennifer lightly.

Dale lifted her shoulders. "It's possible. He's been too busy working since we came back from France to think about sport."

"He must relax sometime."

"He eats," Dale said. "And sleeps." She picked up the portfolio holding her work of the past few weeks, handing it over with some faint reluctance still lingering. "I only finished the top one yesterday, and I haven't started anything else yet. It's just a pastime, of course. I doubt if I'll ever progress beyond watercolors."

Her mother was silent as she went through the small pile, but there was a growing surprise in her eyes.

"But these are good!" she exclaimed at last. "At least, they are to me. I didn't know you were talented this way, Dale."

"I didn't know myself," Dale admitted. "I was interested at school, but there were too many other things to think about." Until this moment she had not acknowledged even to herself how desperately she had needed an outside opinion. "They're all local scenes, of course, and I think I've improved since the first one here. Naturally my technique needs a lot of working on."

"Jos could help you there, couldn't he?" Jennifer put down the last sheet and looked up at her daughter. "You really should let him see them, Dale. He's the obvious one to ask for an opinion."

"No." She closed the portfolio abruptly. "I don't want him to see them."

"Why?" The question was gentle. "Are you afraid he'd laugh at your efforts?"

It was too close to the truth for comfort. Jos cared nothing about feelings. If moved to do so, he could strip her of every shred of confidence in a few words. She wasn't prepared to risk that.

"I just don't want him to see them," she repeated. "Not yet. I'll order tea."

Jennifer didn't move. "When do I get to meet him?"

"Dinner, probably. He's working on two commissions, both with a deadline. He rarely breaks before six."

"Large subjects?"

"I think so. One of the marble blocks measured something like eight-by-four. The floor up there is specially strengthened to take the weight. They take the finished figure out through the window by block and tackle."

"You haven't seen the ones he's working on now?"

"No." Dale moved to the door. "Let's go and find that tea."

She was in the act of pouring it some ten minutes or so later when Jos walked into the room. He was changed into casual slacks and shirt, she saw, stifling her exclamation of surprise. If the effort was in honor of her mother's arrival she appreciated it.

"Nice timing," he said. "We'll need another cup." His glance moved to their visitor, his smile pleasant. "Glad you could make it, Mrs. Ryland."

Her own smile was slower in coming. "I'm only sorry it's taken so long. I have to apologize for Dale's father."

"No consequence." He sat down opposite with his back to the light, blue eyes assessing. "I can see which side of the family Dale inherits her looks from. You're very much alike."

Dale went to fetch another cup from the kitchen, declining to summon assistance. She needed a moment or two to rationalize her thoughts. The look in her mother's eyes a moment ago had needed no defining; not to someone who had experienced that same instant impact herself. Yet why shouldn't her mother feel attracted to Jos? Did a woman in her forties have to be past that kind of experience? After all, she was only a matter of twelve years or so older than he was.

She remembered Jos saying once that age brought out character in a woman. Perhaps in her mother he might see what was lacking in her. She stopped herself sharply there. She couldn't be jealous, could she? Not of her own mother! Ridiculous!

She was in control of herself by the time she got back with the cup. Enough so to meet Jos's eyes without a flicker. He would know there was something on her mind; he always knew. She wouldn't put it past him to guess what she'd been feeling a few minutes ago. Certainly he'd be aware of the impact he'd made. A man like Jos never failed to be aware.

"Sorry I've been so long," she said. "I was talking to Mrs. Girling."

"That's all right," he returned equably. "I took your cup. Jennifer tells me you've been showing her your paintings."

Jennifer already, Dale noted in the brief moment before realization struck her. She felt the warmth rise in her face.

"Only for something to do," she disclaimed. "They're rubbish anyway."

"No they're not." Her mother spoke with authority. "I don't know all that much about art, but I can tell rubbish when I see it. I think you should let Jos see them."

"Don't press it," he said on an easy note. "If Dale wants me to see them I daresay she'll show them to me. It's entirely up to her."

And of total indifference to him, she gathered, and

hardened herself against any lingering desire to follow her mother's advice.

"That's right," she agreed. "Entirely up to me."

"I thought we might eat out tonight in honor of our guest," said Jos as if she hadn't spoken. "Make a break for all of us. Phone L'Etoile and book a table for eight-thirty, will you, Dale."

"Why don't you do it yourself while you're here?" she suggested sweetly. "They're far more likely to give you one at short notice than they are me."

"True," he agreed with an infuriating lack of reaction. "I should have thought of that." He got up. "No time like the present. I'll use the study phone."

There was a small silence after he had left the room. Jennifer was the first to break it.

"Why the daggers drawn?" she asked. "It was a simple enough thing to ask."

Dale shook her head, knowing the cause yet unable to voice it. "He's too fond of sitting back and dishing out the orders. I'm not Mrs. Girling!"

"No, you're Mrs. Blakeman. Mistress of the house." Her mother's tone was light. "You don't act much like it."

"I don't feel much like it," Dale admitted dryly. "All right, so I was being childish. If it's of any interest, it won't pass unremarked. I'm only surprised he let it pass at all. He's a master of the short, sharp response."

"Which doesn't stop you from deliberately drawing it. Like putting your finger through a candle flame, isn't it?"

Dale had to laugh; it was so close to the mark. "You know," she said, "you must be fairly unique as a mother. How is it I never really got to know you before?"

"Because I was too busy trying to be the kind of

mother I should be," came the equable reply. "So busy,
I failed to recognize the other similarities between
us. I'd have blamed myself if you'd made the same mistake I made. Life with a good solid man can be more
hellish than anything if you're not temperamentally
suited to it." The pause was brief, her change of tone
deliberate. "You're still not sure how you feel about
him, are you?"

Dale's smile faded. "Is it that obvious?"

"It is to me. To Jos, too, I'd imagine. He's not exactly dense."

"You like him, don't you?" It was a statement rather
than a question, voice soft.

"Yes, I like him." Jennifer met her eyes quite calmly.
"He's a very vitally attractive man, and I'm not im-
mune from feeling it. If you're going to resent other
women looking at him that way you're going to have a
hard time of it."

"You're not other women. You're my mother."

"And we just got through agreeing I'm untypical of
the species. I'm probably not, when it comes right down
to it. Giving birth doesn't alter character, it simply
buries it under accepted patterns of behavior. You'll
realize that for yourself one of these days."

"I doubt it." Dale kept her voice carefully controlled.
"I don't think Jos wants children."

"Have you discussed it?"

"No." She couldn't bring herself to admit that she
hadn't the courage to bring the subject up. There was no
sense of permanency about this marriage of hers. If Jos
ever wanted out he would take it just as ruthlessly as he
had taken her. Even given the opportunity, she wasn't
sure she wanted his child. It would just be an added
complication.

His return to the room forestalled any further conversation, somewhat to her relief.

"Eight-thirty it is," he confirmed, regaining his seat. "We'll go in by cab then we can all relax."

"Best bib and tucker?" queried Dale brightly. "Or shall we all turn up in Left Bank garb?"

"Sure." His smile was deceptively lazy. "You can wear your painter's smock."

The evening was not, for Dale at least, an enjoyable occasion. She spoke little and drank too much, too well aware of her inability to compete with her mother's quick-witted conversational gambits. It was like seeing someone come to life for the first time, her eyes sparkling as she and Jos sparred amicably through various bones of contention. Jos was the kind of man she should have married all those years ago. He brought out the real Jennifer. He was enjoying doing it, too. That was easy to see. He was never this relaxed with her.

Back at the house, she refused the suggestion of a nightcap with a waspishness she made no attempt to conceal.

"Don't let me stop you though," she said, and was furious when they both took her at her word.

"I'll be up in half an hour," Jos promised, and it was not imagination that made it sound more like a threat. He was good and angry, if concealing it well. She was going to have some answering to do when he did come up.

Preparing for bed, Dale tried to come to terms with her own emotions. She was jealous of her mother, there was no getting away from it. Jennifer still had most of her looks, and retained a slim figure with rigorous control. She didn't look forty-seven, that was a fact.

There was more to it than that though. Her mother was mature; she could meet Jos on his own level. Not for her the insecurity of wondering how long his physical need was going to last; their accord went beyond that. They were in harmony. It was the only word that fitted.

She was in bed when he did come up. She lay feigning sleep while he moved around the room, only opening her eyes when the bathroom door closed behind him. Half an hour, he had said, but it had been closer to an hour. What had they found to talk about down there all that time?

Not her, she hoped. She could bear anything but having herself dissected by the two people who meant the most to her. Should mean the most, she corrected mentally a bare moment later. That was the trouble: she wasn't even sure how she felt about her mother anymore. Was she capable of loving anybody without restriction: as they were, not as she wanted them to be?

In spite of it all, she was on the verge of sleep when Jos slid into the kingsized bed, coming awake with a jerk as he reached for her.

"Don't," she said, pushing at his bare chest with both hands. "I don't want you!"

"But you're going to get me," he came back grimly. "Like it or not!" He came on top of her in one swift movement, pinning her down under him, his face hard boned and unrelenting.

"Jos, no." This time her tone was lower, asking rather than telling, but by no means pleading. "If I behaved badly tonight it was because—"

"*If* you behaved badly!" The anger was still there in him. "You acted like some jealous teenager!"

"Didn't I have reason?" she flashed, ignoring the vulnerability of her position. "You and my mother—it was disgusting!"

"There's nothing disgusting about your mother," he

said with deliberation. "She's a very attractive woman badly in need of a full-blooded love affair."

"Then why don't you give it to her? You're more than capable!"

The sting of his hand across her cheek was shock enough to pull her up short. She gave a muffled sob and tried to hit him back, failing because he jerked his own head out of the way.

"I hate you!" she flung at him viciously. "God, how I hate you!"

She was still saying it in her mind when he took her some minutes later, but her body refused to agree. It always refused to agree. Jos saw to that. He could summon response from a statue if he put his mind to it.

"I don't give a damn how you feel about me," he said on a low rough note when it was over. "This is all I need."

She turned away from him numbly when he let her go, staring into the darkness with aching eyes. She had it in black and white now. He just didn't care. Whatever she did or said to him, it didn't reach him; not where it mattered. All she could do was make him angry.

So all was right, she told herself in sudden bitter resolution. If anger was the only emotion he was capable of feeling, then she'd give him a surfeit of it!

# CHAPTER EIGHT

JENNIFER WENT HOME on the Thursday evening, driven by Jos who refused to listen to any protests.

"No woman can afford to take the risk of going back to an empty house alone these days," he said. "I can at least see you in and check the place over."

"It's going to take all evening," Jennifer pointed out, her glance flicking to her daughter who had so far made no comment. "Why don't you come, too, Dale, then Jos would have company on the way back."

There was no response from Jos. Dale glanced once at the set of his features and quelled any impulse she might have had to agree.

"I'll stay here," she said. "Catch up on my reading." She gave her mother a bright smile, almost hating her yet at the same time sorry to see her go. "I hope the American trip comes off for you. It could be fun."

"It could be a lot of things," came the dry reply, "but I doubt if fun would be one of them. Take care of yourself, darling."

"Oh, I have Jos to do that for me," she returned, borrowing the dryness. She didn't look at him but was still aware of his eyes moving to her with hard intent. He would take care of her all right—in his own inimitable way. It was all they had.

Alone at last she ignored the book she had been threatening to read for days and strolled down to the river, viewing the craft tied up at the landing dock with brooding eyes. Jos had shown her how to handle it but warned her against taking it out alone until she was more proficient in coming back alongside. The last time she had tried it she had opened the throttle instead of killing the engine, and would have rammed the dock had Jos not seized control of the wheel in the nick of time and steered them clear. He had been more derisive than angry, she remembered—the way most men were with a woman who failed to handle mechanical objects with quite their own style and skill. *I have half a mind*, she thought now, *to take the damned boat out right this minute and prove him wrong.*

Half a mind would be about right, she acknowledged wryly a moment later. Where would a gesture like that get her? She could sink the boat and it wouldn't make any difference to the way Jos felt about her. She was simply his possession, nothing else.

And her mother? The question was like a cancer eating at her mind. The attraction was not all one-sided, that she knew. In the past two days she had watched it grow, reducing the years between them to nothing. Jos hadn't wanted her with them tonight; he had made that obvious. Yet if she had no trust in him she must surely have it in her own mother?

Deep down she knew it didn't have to follow. Before anything else her mother was a woman—a desperately lonely woman too long deprived of an adequate outlet for her stronger passions. If Jos made the move would she be able to resist? Would she even want to resist? There were times, as Dale knew to her own cost, when all outside considerations became nothing compared with the overwhelming need of the moment.

She should never have married Jos, she acknowledged

numbly as she walked back to the house. No matter what the incentive, she should have had the strength of mind to turn down a union that even then she had known could never work. If there was any soft core to him at all it was one she didn't know how to reach. She wasn't even sure she wanted to reach it anymore.

Whatever uncertainty there was left in her hardened slowly into acceptance as the hours crept by. The sound of the car returning just after midnight brought no relief, only a blind, surging anger that had to have outlet.

She was brushing her hair when Jos came into the bedroom, the strokes long and deep and deliberate. Seen through the mirror, his face was expressionless, not that she had expected it to be anything else.

"You've been a long time," she said.

"Yes." He took off the cord jacket and slung it casually across a chair back, running a hand through his hair in a gesture denoting weariness. "We got involved—"

"I'm sure you did!" The calmness was gone from her voice, replaced by bitter contempt. "Mother and daughter—it makes a real cozy arrangement, doesn't it? I suppose I should be grateful you're willing to keep it in the family!"

He had his back to her but he had gone very still. When he turned it was slowly, his gaze moving over her almost contemplatively.

"You should be grateful for a lot of things," he said softly. "Not least among them being that you have a mother like Jennifer at all. If you want the truth, I'd have been more than ready to follow any lead she might have given me tonight, but fortunately, or unfortunately, depending on one's viewpoint, she thinks far too much of her only daughter to indulge her own instincts.'' The glitter grew in his eyes. ''I'd make you go and apologize to her if it didn't mean letting her know how little real feeling you have for her.''

''You wanted her.'' It was little more than a whisper. ''I know how difficult it is to say no to you, Jos!''

''You know how difficult *you* find it to say no,'' he came back brutally. ''And mean it, at any rate. You're incapable of feeling anything deeply for anyone or anything, Dale.''

''And you are?'' Her face was white. ''Wouldn't you say we were two of a kind?''

''Perhaps.'' He sounded suddenly tired. ''In which case we'd better decide to settle for what we've got because it obviously isn't going to get any better.''

''I won't sleep with you,'' she said. ''Not anymore.''

His smile came faint and mocking. ''You will—in both senses. If this is the closest we're going to get then we'll indulge it to the full.''

Watching him sit down to take off his shoes, Dale knew herself lost. She could resist him but it wouldn't stop him. She never had been able to stop him.

*I hate him*, she thought, and knew it only partly true. What she felt for him right now was far too complex an emotion to come under one simple heading.

IT WAS ALMOST TWO WEEKS before Dale saw her mother again. Bumping into her quite by accident in Selfridge's one morning, she felt the guilt strike through her at the memory of her suspicion. It made her voice overly bright as she greeted her.

''I should have phoned you before this,'' she said apologetically, ''but what with one thing and another....'' She left it there with the self-depreciating shrug of one too well aware of the lack of adequate excuse. "How's father?"

"Missing you, though he won't admit it." Jennifer's eyes were shrewd. "You look a bit under the weather yourself. Any special reason?"

"I've just recovered from one of those summer colds. They leave you feeling absolutely washed out for a while." Dale tried to sound natural about it. "Do you feel like some coffee?"

"I was just on my way," the other admitted.

She waited until they were seated with the cups in front of them before asking after Jos, her voice casual yet with an undercurrent that gave her away. Catching Dale's eye, she gave a rueful little smile.

"I've missed my conversations with your husband. He's an exceptional man. Marvelous in an emergency, too. I'll never forget how fast he organized help when that car crashed right in front of us. He had the police and an ambulance on the spot within ten minutes."

Dale put down her cup carefully; she could feel her hand trembling. "What car crash?"

"You mean he didn't tell you?" Her mother sounded strange. "That's odd. I wanted him to call you from home and tell you we'd been held up, but he said he'd rather not wait. Surely you wondered where he'd got to?"

There was no element of humor in Dale's sudden desire to laugh. She bit hard on her lip, seeing her mother's expression slowly change and acknowledging the need for honesty between them.

"Yes," she said, "I wondered. Only I supplied my own answer before he had a chance to give me his." She made herself meet and hold the other's gaze, her smile as wry as Jennifer's own had been a moment or two ago. "I accused him of staying on to be with you. I thought the two of you...." Her voice petered out.

Jennifer looked back at her without either moving or speaking for a long moment, something unfathomable in the brown eyes.

"And what did he tell you?" she asked at last.

"He said if it had been up to him it could have happened, but you weren't willing—or words to that effect."

"Men!" The exclamation was soft. "Naturally, you believed him."

"I had no reason to disbelieve him. I knew how drawn to each other the two of you were."

"Yes, you could call it that." There was a certain wistfulness in the statement. "But the physical side of it was all mine."

Dale shook her head in swift repudiation. "He told me he found you attractive."

"There's a difference between that and being attracted in the purely physical sense."

"That's not the impression he gave me."

For a moment there was silence while Jennifer seemed to struggle with something within herself. Finally she sighed.

"Dale, what I'm going to say doesn't show me up in a very good light, but it's about the only way I'm going to convince you." She paused then and took a drink of her coffee as if to steady herself, not lifting her eyes. "The truth is, I lost my head that night Jos drove me home. Without going into detail, I made it pretty clear to him that I was available any time he gave the word. He was very kind about it, very considerate—said he understood that women my age often went through these emotional crises, but he wasn't the one to resolve it for me." This time she did look up, lips twisted. "Not much of a mother, am I, trying to steal my own daughter's husband?"

Dale looked back at her, shaken and uncertain, wanting to believe yet even now doubting.

"Why should he say what he did if it wasn't the truth?" she asked at last with a tremor in her voice. "Why should he twist things around like that?"

Jennifer made a small movement of her head. "I'd like to think he was doing it for my sake, but I've a feeling pride was probably the ruling factor. He wanted to hurt you, the way you must have hurt him."

"I can't hurt him," Dale said bitterly. "He's incapable of being hurt by anyone!"

"Incapable of showing it perhaps. I think he must have once been hurt, very badly, a long time ago so he grew a thick skin over his emotions, but they're still there inside him waiting for the day when someone manages to break through. You could do it, if you really tried—if you wanted to reach him that way."

"I do." It was a whisper.

"Not badly enough or you'd put more effort into it. You said once that he didn't have to marry you, he could have had you without. Yet he still went ahead and did it. And what have you given him—apart from the obvious?" Her voice was low but biting. "You won't even let him see your paintings because you're afraid of a little criticism."

"You really think that would help?"

"It would be a start." The fire went out of her suddenly, leaving her flat and empty. She began to gather her things together. "It's time I was going. I've said more than enough."

"What are you going to do?" asked Dale quietly. "About your own life, I mean."

"Do?" She sat still for a moment, face bleak beneath the smoothly styled sweep of her hair. The pulling together was an obvious physical effort. "I'm going to do what your husband told me to do, and stop wishing for the moon," she stated firmly. "Like he said, very few people are fortunate enough to have everything, and I've left it a bit too late to start radically changing my life in the hope of finding it."

There was nothing Dale could add to that. Nothing she felt qualified to add. She said instead, "When am I going to see you again?"

Her mother's regard warmed. "Do you want to see me again after what I've told you?"

"Of course." She put out an impulsive hand to cover the one at rest on the table. "You didn't have to tell me. You could have let me go on thinking the way I was." Her tone was unsteady. "I love you."

Jennifer returned the pressure, eyes misty. "Tell that to Jos," she urged. "It's what he needs to hear. He might not respond right away, but you can make him believe it in the end."

Providing he wanted to believe it, Dale thought numbly. Jos didn't care what she felt for him; he had said as much. Or had that been pride, too? Perhaps her mother was right and the first intimation of deeper feeling must come from her. It was something to think about.

It was almost four-thirty before she got back to the house. Taking her parcels upstairs, she undressed swiftly and got under a warm shower, feeling the tension ease a little as her muscles relaxed.

Wrapped in a knee-length, white bathrobe with her

hair swathed in a towel, she went back to the bedroom to find Jos already there, a cigarette smoldering in his fingers as he turned from the window.

"Had a good day?" he asked. "You don't seem to have bought much."

"There wasn't much I needed." Dale walked across to the bed, aware of the constriction between them and wondering a little cynically what his reaction would be if she went to kiss him hello the way any normal wife might after a day apart. All very well for her mother to talk about breaking down the barriers, but she didn't have it to do. It wasn't even certain there was a way through. They had been up too long.

"I thought you'd still be in the studio," she added without turning her head. "You usually are at this time."

"I decided I'd had enough for today," he returned. "I didn't seem to be getting anywhere so there wasn't much point in continuing."

She swung to look at him then, reticence forgotten for the moment. "You mean you're having difficulty completing this present work?"

"In a word, yes." His shoulders lifted. "I've been through periods like this before. It will pass. What I need is to leave it alone for a few days—maybe try something else." He paused there, eyes sliding the length of her body down to her bare calves with a look she knew only too well. "Right now I can think of one excellent therapy for a tired mind."

"No!" The retort was sharp—too sharp. She made some attempt to qualify it. "I'm not in the mood, Jos."

"That can be remedied." He reached out and stubbed the remains of the cigarette in the ashtray on the windowsill beside him, the blue eyes unrelenting as he moved purposefully toward her. "I own the copyright, remember."

There was no denying the surge of response as he took her in his arms. It was like a flame leaping through her body, impervious to all attempts to douse it. In the brief moments before she abandoned herself to it, Dale wondered why she needed anything beyond this—why anyone would. Right now it seemed sufficient unto itself.

She had the answer, of course, the way she always did in the end. When Jos left her he left her totally, becoming a stranger again even while he still held her close in his arms. Looking up into the veiled blue eyes, she had a vision of endless years stretching ahead filled with the same emptiness, and knew she couldn't take it. Whatever pain might come from loving Jos it had to be better than the agony of denying herself all emotion.

She made the first tentative move that evening after dinner with a request for him to look at her daubs, as she diffidently called them, and tell her what he thought of her potential talent.

He went through all she had done without comment and without expression, reminding her of the day she had brought the outline of the interview out here for him to see. Long before he had finished she had the aching certainty that his verdict was going to be much the same.

"What do you want me to tell you?" he asked in the end. She had to force herself to answer.

"The truth. Am I any good?"

His shrug told her all she needed to know. "As good as any other dabbler I've seen—maybe even a little better than some. You've a fair technique and you lay in your color quite well."

"But?" she prompted, aware that there had to be one.

"You lack any originality," he told her bluntly. "You paint the way you write—sticking to the rules." He assessed her reaction with a faint smile. "Hardly so important, is it? You don't have to make a living from it."

Dale shook her head, avoiding his eyes. "Seems I'm destined to be second-rate at everything," she said on a purposefully bright note, and drew a suddenly impatient movement from him.

"If you can't take criticism don't ask for it. Anyway, you've hardly given yourself a fair chance. Join a class. Develop your own style. You might not be another Turner but you could eventually produce something worthwhile." He turned away then as if tiring of the whole subject. "Come and finish your coffee."

She went because there was no point in staying, not at all sure that she would be coming back. She had put so much into these past few weeks, and nothing had come through. Was there any use in trying to take it any farther?

As much use as in trying to take anything else any farther, she acknowledged barely a moment later. If she accepted defeat in this, what chance did she stand of getting through to Jos? There might be limitations in both respects but it was up to her to find them.

"I saw my mother in town today," she said over coffee. "She told me about the accident you were involved in." Her eyes came up to find his, meeting the unresponsive blueness with a feeling that the limitations had already caught her up. "She also told me the rest of it," she plodded on doggedly. "I'm sorry, Jos. I misjudged you."

"You didn't misjudge me," he came back levelly. "Not altogether. I didn't find the offer itself so unpalatable."

"But you despise her for making it." She stared at him for a moment, trying to reconcile the version she had heard that morning with what she was reading in the line of his mouth right now. "You told her you understood."

"The motivation perhaps. That doesn't mean I have to approve the act. Your mother was thinking of no one but herself at that moment. Not you, nor your father—not even me in essence; I was just the instrument. If I let her down gently it was only because I didn't trust myself to say what I really felt without going too far the other way. Not that I should have been so surprised. I've yet to meet the woman who puts anything before her own interests."

"Including me?" Her voice was low.

His lips widened briefly and mirthlessly. "You'd like to think you're an exception, is that it? Like hell you are! If you'd been thinking of anyone but yourself you'd have given Roger his marching orders without me having to lift a finger to bring it about. You wanted a fallback in case I didn't come through."

Dale was sitting on the edge of her seat, face flushed, eyes hot. "And who were *you* thinking of when you made sure Roger would see that sculpture? If I'm guilty then you are, too, Jos!"

"I gave you plenty of chances," he said. "A whole month. What were you doing in that time if you weren't cheating him? Did you stop kissing him back when he kissed you, for instance? Did you even bother to tell him you had any doubts?" He shook his head at the look on her face. "It's true, and you know it. Not that you're ever likely to admit it, even to yourself."

Sitting there looking at him, Dale wondered bleakly how she could ever have imagined a time when that shell might crack. He was invulnerable—so tightly encased in his armor that nothing would ever get through.

"Why did you marry me?" she asked on a husky note. "You didn't have to."

"Call it precautionary. It gave me some legal hold over you. Without it you could have walked out at any time."

"I still could."

"Try it," he said, "and I'll fetch you back. Wherever you go, I'll fetch you back." He was twisting the stem of his brandy glass in his fingers, his eyes on her face and a smile on his lips. "You're mine, darling, bodily at least, and that's really all I care about. I'll wring your lovely neck if you ever try to cheat on me, so be warned. Don't follow in your mother's footsteps."

"Jos, why?" She had to make the appeal; it was wrung from her. "What made you this way?"

The smile faded, his mouth taking on a harder line. "No psychoanalysis thanks. I can do my own. Just settle for what you've got out of the deal. In the long run it's easier that way." He drained the brandy left in the glass in one swallow, and got to his feet. "I'm going to work. Don't wait up."

It was a long time before Dale could bring herself to move after he had left the room. She felt drained. What manner of woman could have wreaked that kind of damage, she wondered numbly. And how? She remembered him telling her that night in the fen's house that he had once been involved and it hadn't worked out, but there had been no hint of anything like this.

There had to be a cause though. No man was born with a built-in mistrust of the whole female sex. Somewhere back in his past lay the answer; buried but not forgotten. The question was, how did one go about exorcising it?

It was a question she was to ponder many times during the following days, still without reaching any farseeing conclusions. Sometimes she was moved to ask herself wearily if it really mattered. Jos provided most of what she could ask for in a husband. Why look for more?

She knew why, of course, because it wasn't enough. It never had been enough. She was in love with a man incapable of emotion, and she was only just beginning to learn how bitter a state that could be.

The commissions Jos had been working on were finished in time and duly packed and dispatched. Never having seen either work, Dale had only the vaguest of ideas as to their actual form, although Jos had mentioned once that they were a complementary pair scheduled to grace the outer lobby of a large new art gallery in the north of England. Her reluctance to visit the studio was difficult to explain with any lucidity, yet deep down she knew it stemmed from the fact that the bronze *Shades* was still in residence. She didn't want to see it again. Not the way things were. She had the disturbing feeling that of the two of them, Jos preferred the inanimate image. It was the only one he could trust.

His announcement that he would be away for a couple of days came almost as a relief. Some municipality in Kent wanted to honor one of its more notable historical characters with a monument in the museum grounds, and had asked him to visit the town to discuss designs.

Not his usual kind of thing, he admitted, but it could be interesting. He made no attempt to ask Dale to go with him, leaving her with the impression that he, too, welcomed the break.

It occurred to her only after his departure that now would be the time to make the break total if she were so minded. By the time he came home again she could be gone where he would never find her.

Yet to do that meant cutting herself off from everyone and everything else, she realized hollowly. Anything had to be better than that kind of loneliness. What she and Jos had might not be perfect, but what was? He had told her mother to stop wishing for the moon. It was advice she herself might learn to follow.

# CHAPTER NINE

REGARDLESS OF EVERYTHING, she found herself missing Jos that evening. As a companion he could hardly be bettered, knowledgeable on so many subjects and always ready to listen to her ideas. If sex could be kept out of it they would have a fair relationship, she thought dryly as she poured herself coffee from the pot Mrs. Girling had brought in. Yet did she want sex left out of it? Jos the lover was every woman's dream. That had to make up for a lot.

She was on her second cup when George called through from the gate around eight-thirty to say there was a caller.

"Says he's related to Mr. Blakeman," he advised Dale skeptically. "Name of Darrowby. Never seen him before though. And Mr. Blakeman never said anything about him, either."

Could be a journalist, Dale supposed, but she doubted it. It was too stupid a cover to use even if it were known that Jos himself wasn't home at present. As far as she knew, the marriage was still a well-kept secret. Jos had wanted it that way. The only people who could have leaked it would be her parents, and that was out of the question.

On impulse, and because she rather desperately needed some distraction, she told George to let the man through, assuring him she was ready to accept all responsibility for doing so. Jos had never mentioned any living relatives, but this could quite well be some distant one he hadn't seen for a long time.

She went to the door herself to meet him, opening it before he had time to ring the bell and looking into surprised hazel eyes. He was a little above medium height, and wiry in build, with a thin but attractive face beneath the fairish hair.

About twenty-six or seven, Dale guessed; certainly no more than that. There was no point of resemblance with Jos that she could see.

"You're Jos's wife?" he asked with a convincing lack of formality. "I could hardly believe it when that chap on the gate told me there was a Mrs. Blakeman." He held out his hand, his smile uncertain. "Paul Darrowby. Jos might have mentioned me."

"I'm afraid he hasn't," she confessed. "You'd better come in and do the telling for him."

She took him to the drawing room where a fire burned against the unseasonal chill of the evening, inviting him to a seat and viewing him with interest mixed with speculation. He was well enough dressed in the checked trousers and light jacket, but his clothing lacked the cut and style of first-class tailoring. Bought off the rack, she would have said—and recently. To impress whom?

"Would you like a drink?" she asked, and saw the smile come again.

"Sounds good. Scotch, please."

He waited until she was pouring the liquid before adding, "I gather Jos isn't home at present."

"That's right." She brought the glass across to him, taking her own gin and lime to the chair opposite and eyeing him questioningly. "What is the actual relationship?"

"Brothers," he said. "By adoption. Difficult to explain to someone like that man on the gate so I didn't even try."

Dale stared at him blankly for a moment before realization came. "You mean you were adopted by Jos's parents?"

"No," he said. "My parents adopted Jos. I came along later. They tell me it often happens that way. He took the name Blakeman by deed poll when he left home. Said Darrowby wasn't his to keep anyway."

A glimmer of some emotion as yet undefined stirred at the back of Dale's mind. "I didn't know," she said slowly. "He never told me he was adopted."

"He never liked admitting it. In fact he hated the whole idea." Paul hesitated for a moment, eyeing the drink in his hand with an odd expression. "You see, my parents made the mistake of not telling him the truth while he was young enough to adapt. When he did find out it was too late."

"How did he find out?"

"By accident when he was sixteen. Came across the adoption papers when he was looking for something in dad's desk one day. It bowled him over, and I'm afraid I didn't help any. I was eight at the time. That's a big age gap even between real brothers. I overheard him asking my mother about it and crowed in his face because I was a real Darrowby and he wasn't. A ripe case of sibling jealousy, I suppose. They had to pull him off me—although he didn't really do much harm. After that he was never the same. He got a job as soon as he could get out of school, and put himself through an advanced art course in his spare time. He was brilliant even then. Everybody said so. We didn't see much of him once he was able to keep himself. He just cut himself off."

The feeling inside her was crystallizing into one big ache. Trying to imagine how she would have felt over a discovery like that at sixteen was useless because she wasn't Jos. The reaction would be totally individual, dependent on the very nature of the person to whom the situation applied. Jos was proud; he had probably always been proud. He would have felt like an outsider; no longer the eldest son of the family but a poor second best. It explained so much about the hardness in him, if not all. He had been stripped of his very birthright at a time when he was least able to withstand the loss.

"If you've seen so little of him over the years, why have you come now?" she heard herself asking, and had a sense of premonition about the answer even before Paul made it.

"I'm in trouble," he said. "Jos is the only one I can turn to."

Dale looked at him for a moment, trying to analyse the depth of sincerity in the hazel eyes. "Financial trouble?"

There was misery in his answering nod. "Yes."

"What makes you think Jos might be prepared to help you?"

He spread his hands in a gesture she had used herself on countless occasions. "Like I said, he's the only one left to try. If he won't...." He left it there, jaw suddenly clenching. When he spoke again it was on a carefully controlled note. "I'd have thought your marriage would have made big news."

"He made sure it didn't." She should have said we, Dale realized at once, but it was too late now. "We didn't want publicity," she tagged on, only slightly overemphasizing the word.

"How long? I mean, when did it happen?"

"Just a few weeks ago."

"I don't even know your name," he said.

She told him, still trying to straighten out her thoughts. She was probably going to be in trouble with Jos for inviting Paul into the house in the first place. Faced with a demand for money on top of it, she barely knew what his reaction might be.

"Look, Paul," she said impulsively. "I don't know why you need money, and I don't want to know, but if I were you I'd try writing to Jos about it first."

There was a kind of resignation in the hazel eyes as he looked back at her. "I can't wait that long," he said. "I have to have it by Monday. When will Jos be back?"

"Tomorrow night, I think. Perhaps not until Friday. It depends how things go." She studied him uncertainly, sensing the held-in desperation. "Perhaps you'd better talk to me about it after all. I don't know whether I can help, but at least I can listen."

The movement of his head was slow. "I can't burden you with my problems. I shouldn't be here at all."

"But you have nowhere else to go," she reminded him. "Just tell me. A trouble shared is a trouble halved—and all the other clichés. First of all, how much do you need?"

It took him a moment to say it. When he did it was swiftly, as if to minimize the figure. "Eight hundred pounds."

Dale let out her breath in a small sigh, sitting back in the chair. "More than I can do anything about on my own, I'm afraid. I might scrape about a hundred together with luck."

He was looking at her oddly. "You'd have given me that if it'd been enough? A total stranger?"

"Hardly a stranger. You and Jos grew up together. That has to mean something."

"You don't even know yet why I need it," he said. "You might not be as generously inclined when you do." He paused, taking a drink from the glass in his hand as if for courage, then putting it down without meeting her eyes. "I borrowed the money over a longish period from the firm I work for. I'm in a position to have access to the books. I thought I could straighten things out eventually, but I reckoned without things like spot audits. They're starting Tuesday. If I could replace the actual cash in the account I could get around the rest. I might collect a rap over the knuckles for bad bookkeeping, but they couldn't prove anything."

"Was it gambling?" Her tone was gentle.

He shook his head, smile wry. "I met this woman. Older than me by a few years, but like nobody I'd ever met before. The only thing was, she was used to better things than I could afford to give her—best seats at the theater, good restaurants, et cetera. I started taking the money a little at a time to supplement my income, until it got out of hand in the end."

"I take it you don't see her anymore?"

"Not since I realized I was being taken for a ride. I was an idiot. I should have seen through her from the first. A woman like that doesn't bother with somebody like me unless they're on the make. Not that I expect Jos to accept blind stupidity as any excuse. I shouldn't imagine he ever allowed anything like that to happen to him." He glanced up then, assessing her expression with a faint surprise. "No censure?"

Dale smiled a little. "None worth talking about. I don't suppose you're going to go through this again by choice."

"Not if I get away with it." His face clouded again. "*If*. Even if Jos does get back tomorrow, I still have to enlist his sympathies. Unless he's altered radically since I last saw him, that isn't going to be easy."

Dale couldn't deny it. As far as she could tell, Jos hadn't altered at all.

"Do you have to be at work tomorrow?" she asked, coming to a swift decision. "Can you get any time off?"

"I've got it," he said. "I took three days owing me to try and raise the money." His shoulders lifted wryly. "Most loan companies are out, and my bank manager certainly wouldn't play. He refused me an overdraft only a couple of weeks ago, and that was for household expenses. If he won't entertain those he's hardly likely to look very favorably on a request for eight hundred, reason unspecified."

"You're married?" Dale was hard put to keep the surprise from her voice.

He sensed it anyway, the wryness increasing. "Makes it even worse, doesn't it? Lisa's visiting her mother at the moment. We haven't been getting along too well these past few months. If I'd helped myself to this money for her sake it might have made some sense. We're always so chronically short."

Dale was silent for a long moment. She wasn't the only one with problems. "Stay here tonight," she said. "Tomorrow night, too, if Jos doesn't get back. At least you'll be on the spot when he does come."

"I couldn't," he said, but there was hesitation in his voice.

"Yes, you could. Anything's better than hanging around an empty house. Anyway," she added firmly, "you'd be company for me."

Paul relaxed suddenly, his whole face revealing the

strain he had been under. "Thanks," he said gruffly.
"You don't know what it cost me to come here at all."

"I can guess." Dale glanced at the carriage clock on
the mantlepiece then back to his face. "Have you
eaten?"

"Not since breakfast," he confessed. "Haven't felt
much like it."

"Well, you ought to have something." She got up.
"Stay there while I go and arrange it. I won't be long."

She didn't bother calling Mrs. Girling. It took only a
few minutes to make a pile of ham sandwiches and another pot of coffee. Not exactly a feast, but it would
suffice for the present. In a little while she would see
about arranging a room for him, too. Mrs. Girling
would have to be informed about that, of course. Not
that it made any difference. The housekeeper took her
orders from the mistress of the house, not vice versa.

Paul was sitting where she had left him, staring into
the fire with a lost look around the thin features.

"Eat these," she said, putting the tray down on the
table at his side and removing the empty glass. "The
coffee will do you more good than any more of this."

He didn't argue about that, taking hold of a sandwich
with a lack of interest that faded on the first bite. He
looked up at her then and smiled. "These are good. Did
you make them yourself?"

"With my own fair hands. I wasn't born to a life of
leisure."

"How did you and Jos meet?" he asked, taking another sandwich. "He's quite a bit older than you, isn't
he?"

"Twelve years," she admitted. The pause was brief.
"I went to interview him for a magazine article."

"In *World*, was it? I remember reading that and wondering what kind of person it took to get through that guard he's put between himself and the media. Bit of a recluse, isn't he?''

"I suppose you could call it that.'' Dale didn't particularly want to talk about the man she had married. What Paul had told her made some difference, but not enough. They were as far apart as they had every been—perhaps even farther than she imagined, as Jos had never felt moved to tell her about his background himself.

She sat back and put her neglected drink to her lips, watching Paul demolish the sandwiches with the air of a man under grateful if temporary reprieve. A weak character, perhaps, yet she liked him. At least he recognized his weaknesses. She hoped Jos would see fit to help him out in this instance. He was so obviously desperate. There had to be some kind of tie there, no matter what the circumstances. They had been brothers for eight years—in the eyes of the law they were brothers still. Surely not even Jos could turn his back on a situation such as the one Paul was in right now.

But he could, and she knew it. Jos could do whatever it moved him to do. Nor did it help very much to know the reason for his inability to feel for others. In fact it underlined a certain weakness on his part because he had allowed it to color his whole life. No matter how painful the truth had been, Paul's parents had provided him with a home and a family, had given him their name. They had deserved better than the treatment he had meted out.

Mrs. Girling was surprised but uncomplaining when asked to prepare a room for their guest. Dale found Paul a pair of Jos's pyjamas, the jacket of which he never wore anyway—handing them over with a light injunction to roll up the trouser legs for a better fit.

"The Darrowby males are all small statured," he acknowledged with a tired smile. "Even as a boy I could never quite understand why Jos was so much taller than dad. Heredity's a strange thing, isn't it. He must often have wondered what his real parents were like. Don't imagine he ever traced them."

"I shouldn't think it was possible after all that time," Dale agreed. "I'll see you in the morning, Paul. And try not to worry too much." She was mentally crossing her fingers as she said it. "I'm sure Jos will want to help."

Jos had to help, she told herself later, lying alone in the king-sized bed for the first time in weeks. She wouldn't let him turn Paul away. Eight hundred pounds was a small price to pay for all the years of repudiation.

THE DETERMINATION was still with her the following day, communicating itself to Paul in some indefinable way. They spent the morning lazily on the terrace in a warmth totally at odds with the previous day's weather. With only a little prompting on Dale's part, he told her about his marriage and the difficulties involved in setting up a home on a shoestring. They couldn't yet afford to have the child both of them wanted, he admitted disconsolately, because Lisa needed to keep her job in order to pay the mortgage. It was money, or the lack of it, that was slowly driving them apart.

It was in an effort to cheer him up a little that Dale suggested taking the boat out on the river, prepared to trust his male expertise in bringing them safely in to land again. She remained undaunted when he told her he had never done any boating before. If she damaged it, she damaged it, and that was all there was to it. Jos could afford to pay for repairs, even if the insurance didn't cover learner drivers.

It turned out to be one of the happiest afternoons she had spent in ages. Even Paul seemed to forget why he was here and simply settled to enjoying it. Coming back in time for tea, Dale set her teeth and steered for the landing dock with a prayer in her heart, letting out her breath on a relieved note of laughter when they came alongside with scarcely a bump.

"I can tell you now," she said, "that I wasn't at all sure I could get us in without taking a bath. Last time I tried it, I almost took the side off!"

Paul's answering laugh died in his throat as his eyes traveled the length of the garden to the terrace and the man standing there.

"Your husband is back," he said flatly.

Jos watched them coming without moving a muscle. He was still wearing the clothes in which he had traveled, his face cold above the conventional white shirt.

"Having fun?" he inquired.

"Trying," Dale said, determined not to give way to any weakening of her resolve. "Did you see the way I brought the boat in? Not a scratch!"

"I saw." His tone was short, his eyes still on Paul. "What are you doing here?"

"He came to see you," Dale put in, and froze before the glance he turned on her.

"He can speak for himself."

Paul made the effort, face reflecting a sudden desire to be elsewhere right at this moment. "Dale's right, I did come to see you, Jos. I...." He broke off, mouth tensing. "Can we discuss it somewhere else?"

"Why not? You seem to have had free run of the house while you've been here. Where would you suggest?" He didn't wait for any answer, swinging around toward the house. "Come on. Both of you. Let's get this sorted out."

He went no farther than the drawing room, confronting the two of them with a steely glint in his eyes.

"Let's have it. I take it this isn't purely a social call?"

"I'll leave you alone," said Dale, sensing Paul's reticence. She made a move toward the door, stopping abruptly as Jos held up a staying hand.

"No, you don't. You let him in, you'll stay and listen. No doubt you've already heard."

"I told her everything," Paul admitted. "I thought—"

"You don't *know* everything," Jos interrupted harshly. "You never did. Supposing you tell me what you came for."

Paul swallowed, his eyes briefly seeking Dale's as if for reassurance. "I'm in trouble," he said. "I wouldn't be here at all if I'd any other place to go. Can you... will you lend me some money, Jos?"

There was absolutely no reaction in the stronger features. "How much?"

"Eight hundred pounds." The lack of hope was apparent both in eyes and voice. "I realize it's a lot but—"

"Why?" The word clipped across his as if he hadn't spoken.

Paul sighed and told him. "I borrowed money from my firm. I have to have it back before the audit on Tuesday. I've tried all the conventional ways of raising it, only it's useless. If I had the time to get a loan through, I couldn't afford the interest rates the sharks charge."

"You might save your job."

"For what? I'd be in the same boat." He paused, searching for a sign—any sign. "Jos, if you're going to say no, for God's sake say it and have done," he burst out at last.

"All right. No." Jos turned away, moving to the liquor cabinet. "Have a whiskey. You look as if you need it. Dale?"

"Nothing thanks." Her voice had a tremor in it. "I'd like to talk to you. Alone."

"If it's on the same subject, the answer is still no." He poured two whiskies and brought the glasses back to where Paul still stood rooted, handing one of them over without altering his expression. "You don't have to be in any hurry. It's been a long time since we met. Sit down and tell me about yourself. You're married, aren't you?"

"Yes." The younger man complied as if in a dream, his hand shaking as it grasped the glass. "What am I going to do?" he asked on a note that went through Dale like a shaft.

"Try facing the music," Jos suggested hardily. "A full confession and a promise to pay the money back might go some way toward mitigation."

"I can't afford to pay it back. Not in any short time, at least. They'll know that." He gave a short, humorless laugh. "They should!"

"Don't try using an inadequate salary as an adequate excuse," came the clipped response. "Thieving is thieving, no matter what the reason for doing it."

"Oh, stop it!" Dale could contain her emotions no longer. Her eyes sparkled with anger—and with disgust. "Who are you to preach, Jos? Do you know what it's like to be so desperately short of money you don't know where to *turn*? *Do* you?"

"Not recently," he admitted, unmoved. "I've gone without in my time."

"Not enough. Not nearly enough! You wouldn't be so damned—"

"Dale, don't." Paul sounded miserable but resolved. "You know why I took the money. You don't have to make up any excuse for me." His eyes sought the blue ones. "I spent it on a woman. Another woman, not my wife. I was a total fool and you're probably right to turn me down." He drained the glass he still held with an air of coming to terms with something, and put it down, getting to his feet in the same movement. "I'll get out of your way."

"Paul, wait!" Dale caught at his arm, holding onto him as she turned back to Jos, pleading in her eyes now. "Lend him the money—please! He'll pay you back in time. I know he will! You can't let him face a possible jail sentence for embezzlement. You just can't!"

He said nothing for a long, long moment; the skin seemed stretched taut over the bones of his face. "Why should it matter so much to you?" he asked at last. "You met him for the first time less than twenty-four hours ago."

"Because he's your brother—even if you won't acknowledge the relationship. You can't go on turning your back on people forever." She pushed Paul gently down into the chair he had just vacated, and crossed to lay a hand on the familiar hardness of another arm, looking up into the lean dark face with entreaty. "Jos, I'm begging you. For your sake as much as Paul's. Don't send your own brother away empty handed."

"Half brother," he corrected. He sounded remote. "It's time the record was put straight. We had the same mother if not the same father."

Paul was staring at him in sheer incredulity. "That's

not true!'' he burst out. "How can it be? You found the adoption papers yourself!"

"I'm not denying it." Jos lifted his own glass to his lips, taking half the contents in one swallow. His eyes, coming back to Dale's face, held an expression hard to decipher. "Your father gave me his name when he and my mother were married. I was three years old at the time, but I'd known him as a father since I was old enough to remember at all, so it didn't change anything."

"I don't understand." Paul echoed Dale's own bewilderment. "Are you trying to say you were illegitimate?"

"No. Mother was married to my father before she met yours. She left him when I was a few months old and went to live with yours. When the divorce came through she married him and had my name changed to his legally."

"With your father's consent?" It was Dale who asked the question, her voice low and shaken.

"Naturally. It couldn't have been done without. I understood he thought it best for me—provide me with a more stable background." He paused there, lips thinning. "He was dead by the time I found out the truth."

"Who was he?" This time it was Paul asking the question. He sounded dazed, obviously still trying to come to grips with this new development to a story he had thought he knew so well.

"Lawrence Blakeman—struggling artist. Made the mistake of letting a woman come between him and his work, and paid the price." He looked at Paul steadily. "Your father offered a future with some promise about it. Safety and security."

"You're saying that's the only reason she married him?"

"No. Women are capable of persuading themselves to any emotion if it gets them what they want. Looking back, I'd say they were happy enough. Especially as your father got on in his job. He was a good man. He provided an excellent home for us all. Pity he had to die so relatively young."

"I don't think he wanted to go on living after mom was killed. He always blamed himself." Paul brought himself visibly down to earth again, eyes clouding afresh as he remembered why he was here. "Why choose now to tell me all this?" he said dully.

"Ask my wife. She seems to have all the answers."

"Jos." Her voice sounded thick in her throat. "I only wanted—" She broke off helplessly in face of the unrelenting coolness in his gaze. "What's the use!"

"I don't have my checkbook on me," he said to Paul over her shoulder. "You'd better come along to the study. Are you going to have time to straighten things out before the audit?"

"I am now. I can go in this weekend and sort out the books." He looked as if he could hardly believe the change of heart, but grateful for it all the same. "Thanks, Jos. I'll pay you back."

"I'd rather you didn't." There was a certain distaste in the statement. "Regard it as paying off some of my debt to your father, if you like."

Pride fought a brief battle with expediency in the younger man's expressive face, and lost. He couldn't afford the gesture. "If that's the way you want it," he said on a gruff note. "I won't bother you again." His glance moved to Dale, taking on a certain regret. "Sorry I dropped you into this mess, but thanks anyway."

"You're welcome." She could no more have looked

at Jos at that moment than fly. "I only hope things work out better for you from now on."

It seemed very quiet in the sunlit room after they had gone. There was some whiskey left in the glass Jos had been using. She picked it up and took a swallow, coughing at the bite of the spirit but needing the warmth it brought. They had won, she and Paul, but she felt no triumph in the fact. She wasn't sure what she felt anymore—about anything.

She was sitting on the longer of the two sofas when Jos came back, the glass still in her hand. He came over and took it from her, finishing off the contents with a swift jerk of his head.

"You don't need that," he said. "It's all over. Your houseguest just went home."

"Our houseguest." Her voice was very quiet. "Can we talk about it?"

"There's nothing to talk about. You got what you wanted."

"I don't mean the money—or Paul. I mean you."

"No." He said it with finality. "Just forget the whole thing."

"The way you have been all these years?" She looked up at him with trembling lips, "Haven't you had enough of bitterness, Jos? What your mother did in not letting you know your father was bad, I agree, but he had a hand in it, too."

"Do you think I don't take that into account?" His tone was suddenly savage. "He wasn't in any position to do anything else considering the circumstances. No court would grant custody to a man without adequate means of support, even if he'd wanted it. He had his work to think about. I can understand that. Better a clean break in the long run."

"Better for who?" she insisted. "Not for you obviously. He could have refused permission for the adoption; claimed access. At least you'd have known who your real father was even if you couldn't live with him."

"Leave it," he said. "You're fighting a lost cause. Seems to be your day for it."

"Except that I won the last one," she reminded him with some bitterness, and heard his short, jarring laugh.

"You didn't win it. I just wanted to see how far you were prepared to go on someone else's behalf. Paul must have made quite an impression on you."

"Yes he did. Probably because he's an ordinary, fallible mortal like the vast majority of us, not some demigod who sets himself up in judgment of others!" It sounded ridiculous even as she was saying it, but she was too miserable to care. "If it's perfection you want, go on up and look at that thing you created. Only it isn't real, Jos, because there's no such thing. You cheated just enough to make it seem so. Raymond Dalby guessed that much."

"Possibly." His mouth was taut. "But I can't share my bed with a bronze image unfortunately, so I still need you around." The anger drained from him suddenly, leaving him blank and emotionless. "I'm going to change."

"Jos," she said his name quietly but with enough emphasis to halt him at the door, waiting until he turned his head to look back at her. Her throat ached; she had to force the words through it. "I'm not staying with you. Not this way. I was a fool to think I could."

"I won't let you go," he stated without raising his voice. "Not until I'm good and ready."

"When will that be?"

"I don't know." The blue eyes held a bleakness she

had never seen there before. "Perhaps never. Don't wait dinner for me. I'll have a tray sent to the studio."

Dale was sitting where he had left her when Mrs. Girling came in sometime later to ask if she wanted tea. Rousing herself to respond to the question, she wondered fleetingly if things might have been different had Jos pursued a life-style more akin to the one they had shared at the fen's house. This house was beautiful but it wasn't a home. She still felt a visitor in it.

Yet would she feel the same way if she and Jos had a more normal relationship? Houses took their atmospheres from the people who lived in them. All this one was doing was reflecting the lack of emotional commitment between the two of them.

Thinking about what she had learned of Jos this afternoon brought a lump to her throat. He had spent a large part of his life hating his mother for robbing him of his real father, and had found little in the women he had known in the ensuing years to convince him that any could be trusted. It would take a long time and a lot of caring to eradicate that damage. What she had to ask herself was did she care enough? Was she capable of caring enough?

Trying to look ahead to a future without Jos, she came finally to the conclusion that there was no future without him—or none that she really wanted. If loving Jos was going to bring her pain then that was something she was going to have to learn to accept, because love him she did. And she owed it to him to tell him so. Not tomorrow or the next day, but now, this very afternoon while the courage was in her.

The studio occupied almost a whole side of the upper floor, facing south to catch the light. She found the door partially ajar, and hesitated only a bare moment before pushing it wider to step over the threshold for the very first time.

Jos was sitting on a trestle with his back half turned to her, bent head supported by a hand under his chin in a pose so reminiscent of a certain Rodin sculpture Dale almost had to smile. Beyond, on a stand, rested the bronze she had seen only once before, burnished by the light above to a golden sheen that caught the breath. She couldn't see his face from where she stood, only judge the weariness in every line of his body.

"I was wrong," he said without turning. "It isn't enough. Not anymore."

She answered very softly. "For me it never was. I love you, Jos."

He swung his head to look at her then, mouth acquiring the familiar slant. "Just like that?"

"Not quite," she admitted. "You're not an easy man to love. Remember what you told me the night you decided we were going to be married?" The tremor in her voice belied any lightness she was trying to infuse into the words. "An overrated emotion, you called it. I tried to run away from you then but you wouldn't let me go."

"I couldn't," he said. "No more than now." He looked at her for a moment, the hunger there in his eyes for her to see. "I'm not sure what you mean by love. What makes it any different from wanting—the way I want you?"

"Tenderness perhaps." Warmth was curling through her. "You've never been tender with me, Jos. Forceful; passionate; wonderfully exciting, but never tender." She went to him then, slipping to her knees in front of him to put her arms around his neck and kiss him the way she felt like kissing him. "That's tenderness," she whispered against his lips. "Slow and gentle. Do you think you could ever manage it?"

"Not all the time." His voice was rough. "The way you make me feel isn't slow and gentle. It's like a fire I can't put out." He moved his hands to cup her breasts, his touch possessive the way it always was. "All I know is I can't have enough of you, Dale. No matter how many times I take you it will never be enough! You're in my blood."

"And you're in mine." Her voice was thick in her throat. "Show me, Jos. Love me your way. The rest will come."

She knew it with certainty now; it was already there inside him. All it needed was release, and that was up to her to provide. It would take time to make him open up completely, but they had plenty of it. The shades were coming down at last.

# What the press says about Harlequin romance fiction...

"When it comes to romantic novels...
Harlequin is the indisputable king."
— *New York Times*

"...exciting escapism, easy reading, interesting
characters and, always, a happy ending...
They are hard to put down."
— *Transcript-Telegram,* Holyoke (Mass.)

"...always...an upbeat, happy ending."
— *San Francisco Chronicle*

"...a work of art."
— *Globe & Mail,* Toronto

"Nothing quite like it has happened since
*Gone With the Wind...*"
— *Los Angeles Times*